VIOLENCE
IN
MODERN
LITERATURE

James A. Gould
University of South Florida

John J. Iorio
University of South Florida

BOYD & FRASER PUBLISHING COMPANY
3627 Sacramento Street, San Francisco, California 94118

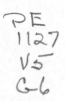
James A. Gould and John J. Iorio: VIOLENCE IN MODERN LITERATURE

Library of Congress Catalog Card Number: 71-182676

ISBN: 0-87835-037-3

3 • 4

TABLE OF CONTENTS

Part One:

THE NATURE OF VIOLENCE

Part Two:

THE LITERATURE OF VIOLENCE

Introduction

VIOLENCE HAS BEEN an endemic part of man's existence since his beginning. The great documents of Western civilization have chronicled the shape and meaning of this violence, and have revealed a phenomenon that has remained remarkably constant in its nature and consequences. Even now across almost six centuries the words of Jean DeMontreuil have a chilling familiarity:

> Who shall tell of the robbery and the burning even of sacred places? Who shall set forth the sacrilege, the raping, the violence, the oppression, the extortion, the plundering, the pillaging, the banditry, and the rioting? Finally, to embrace many crimes in a few words, who will portray the inhuman savageries . . . committed in this horrible and most cruel war?

Despite this dossier of inhumanity, the phenomenon of violence has not been seriously studied until recent times, while the instincts and impulses giving rise to acts of violence have just begun to claim the efforts of the best minds. Today the reality of violence in our lives has become an issue of paramount importance. What evolution was to late nineteenth-century thought, what sex was to early twentieth-century psychology, violence is to the modern imagination.

While the violence of the past reveals its frightening constancy in human affairs, this century, in both its explosive eruptions and attitudes toward violence, appears to be a special case. We are insistently reminded that ours is the most violent of centuries, and that ours is the most violent of societies. There may be some truth to these charges— haunted as we are by the vision of nuclear clouds and traumatized by the enduring stench of concentration camps. At the same time our fears are enhanced by the awareness that value systems of the past which placed some restraint upon violence have today lost their motive force, leaving us defenseless in the face not only of the acts of violence but also against their theoretical justifications. Our times, therefore, appear to be, if not different, at least distinctive with respect to violence.

Our own country, born in revolution, its expansion rimmed by

1

violence, does not escape special consideration. A society which places such high value on competition is bound to produce a vast reservoir of aggression, and aggression, we realize, is a parent of violence.

Our times are distinctive in yet another way. Earlier societies, for example, had accepted violence, especially in its highly organized forms, as an inevitable fact of life. Karl Von Clausewitz, for instance, saw war as an extension of politics by other means. It was Oswald Spengler, the historian, who said, "War is the external form of high existence of mankind, and states exist for the purpose of war." Up to World War I poets usually glorified war. Today, however, these encomia to war have been replaced by a belief (as Marshall F. Gilula and David N. Daniels tell us in "Violence and Man's Struggle to Adapt") that our societies have become too complex, too tenuous to permit violence. Hovering between fragile order and chaos, our culture finds the price of violence exorbitant. While we may have trivialized violence to the point where many have become used to it and accept it as a part of life; while the apocalyptic vision remains strong in the modern imagination, there is at the same time an equally strong disposition to see violence as a phenomenon inimical to life, and an equally strong desire to bring it within some rational control.

But before we can control violence we must first understand its nature and its roots. Immediately we are beset by questions. What is an act of violence? Is it a relative matter? As Newton Garver, attempting to define violence, points out in "The Nature of Violence," "There is more violence in the black qhettos than there is anywhere else in America—even when they are quiet."

And does violence always involve physical force? Can there be psychological violence? When a man screams abusively at his wife, humiliates another person, ridicules a child, is he doing violence even though he does not physically harm another? Is it possible then for social institutions to degrade people and would this constitute violence? Is there a significant psychic distance between the week-end hunter and the search and destroy missions in war? Between the scalping rituals of American Indians and those soldiers in Vietnam who have cut off the ears of Viet Cong dead? Or between the killings at Kent State University and My Lai?

Is violence always destructive? Is it too simple to say, as some psychologists maintain, that it results from frustration? Is it too much to say that it is part of the structure of human personality, fixed and ineradicable? Does it have some creative aspect, as some have held? And what of the non-violence of a Martin Luther King, Jr.? Can that be an alternative to violence, or is it simply another form of violence turned inward?

And what of the justifications of violence? We kill in self-defense. We maim to protect property. We go to war for defense. We beat children for their own good. We employ violence in defense of religion; we have violence for sport and entertainment. Are these justifications always valid?

What is the relationship of violence to aggression? To power? To pleasure? To sex? These and other questions demand consideration before we can meaningfully study the manifestations and meanings of violence in our society.

Most texts have sought to present violence as a concomitant of human endeavors—as a means to other ends. The danger is that the issue of violence may be skirted or superficially treated. The authors have elected instead to see violence as much as possible in terms of its roots, its causes, and its nature. Both the essays and the fiction, which expose the student to a variety of styles and techniques, address themselves to this concern.

While Arthur Schlesinger, Jr. sees violence as a disease determined by the health of the larger community, Gilula and Daniels see it as a central problem in man's adaptive behavior. Garver addresses himself to the problem of definition while Robert Audi seeks out causes of the complexities involved in any justification of violence, especially in a democratic society.

The fiction examples have not been selected to support the ideological thrusts of the essays. They are intended to extend the probing of violence beyond the limitations of the essay. Each selection depicts some nuance, some new gesture, some metaphorical inquiry into the nature and causes of violence. Through the fiction we can examine violence as a middle-class expression, in its social and sexual origins, as part of a religious impulse, as a product of racism and guilt, as political necessity, as a result of insanity or sentimentality.

Through both the essays and fiction the student should become aware of the dimensions of violence and arrive at some intellectual shape of this most important of human problems. At the same time, the selections should improve the student's literary skills. In probing a single issue deeply in the company of accomplished writers, the student should develop an awareness of the variety and effectiveness of literary forms and techniques. He should, in charting the depths of a human experience, come to realize the necessary alliance between the examination of a problem and its verbal articulation.

3

Dedicated to those people who suffered violence at Jackson State, Kent State, Orangeburg and The People's Park.

PART ONE

The Nature of Violence

THE DARK HEART
OF AMERICAN HISTORY*

Arthur Schlesinger, Jr.

ARTHUR SCHLESINGER, JR. was an Associate Professor of History at Harvard, 1946-1954. He became Professor in 1954 and remained there until 1961 when he became a Special Assistant to the President of the United States until 1964. Presently, he is Albert Schweitzer Professor of Humanities at City University of New York. Among his awards are the Pulitzer Prize (1945); Francis Parkman Prize (1957); Bancroft Prize (1958); National Book Award (1965); and Gold Medal, National Institute of Arts and Letters (1967). Some of his books are, Age of Jackson, Age of Roosevelt, Vol. I-III, The Politics of Hope, A Thousand Days: J. F. Kennedy in the White House, *and* The Bitter Heritage. *In the following article, Schlesinger examines some of the history of violence in America, especially the recent murders of prominent political figures. He especially examines the recent violence in America and suggests that the high level is explained by at least two factors: We have been at war for more than twenty consecutive years, and our mass media portray so much violence. Finally, he suggests that America must recognize its responsibility to change this situation.*

THE MURDERS within five years of John F. Kennedy, Martin Luther King, Jr., and Robert F. Kennedy raise—or ought to raise—somber questions about the character of contemporary America. One such murder might be explained away as an isolated horror, unrelated to the inner life of our society. But the successive shootings, in a short time, of three men who greatly embodied the idealism of American life suggest not so much a fortuitous set of aberrations as an emerging

---

pattern of response and action—a spreading and ominous belief in the efficacy of violence and the politics of the deed.

Yet, while each of these murders produced a genuine season of national mourning, none has produced a sustained season of national questioning. In every case, remorse has seemed to end, not as an incitement to self-examination, but as an escape from it. An orgy of sorrow and shame becomes an easy way of purging a bad conscience and returning as quickly as possible to business as usual.

"It would be . . . self-deceptive," President Johnson said after the shooting of Robert Kennedy, "to conclude from this act that our country is sick, that it has lost its balance, that it has lost its sense of direction, even its common decency. Two hundred million Americans did not strike down Robert Kennedy last night any more than they struck down John F. Kennedy in 1963 or Dr. Martin Luther King in April of this year."

I do not quarrel with these words. Of course two hundred million Americans did not strike down these men. Nor, in my judgment, is this a question of a "sick society" or of "collective guilt." I do not know what such phrases mean, but I am certain that they do not represent useful ways of thinking about our problem. Obviously most Americans are decent and God-fearing people. Obviously most Americans were deeply and honestly appalled by these atrocities. Obviously most Americans rightly resent being told that they were "guilty" of crimes they neither willed nor wished.

Still, it is not enough to dismiss the ideas of a sick society and of collective guilt and suppose that such dismissal closes the question. For a problem remains—the problem of a contagion of political murder in the United States in the 1960s unparalleled in our own history and unequaled today anywhere in the world. If we minimize this problem, if we complacently say it is all the work of lunatics and foreigners, that nothing is wrong and that our society is beyond criticism, if we cry like Macbeth: "Thou canst not say I did it; never shake/Thy gory locks at me," then we lose all hope of recovering control of the destructive impulse within. Then we will only continue the downward spiral of social decomposition and moral degradation.

Self-knowledge is the indispensable prelude to self-control; and self-knowledge, for a nation as well as for an individual, begins with history. We like to think of ourselves as a peaceful, tolerant, benign people who have always lived under a government of laws and not of men. And, indeed, respect for persons and for law has been one characteristic strain in the American tradition. Most Americans probably pay this respect most of their lives. Yet this is by no means the only strain in our tradition. For we also have been a violent people. When we refuse to acknowledge the existence of this other strain, we refuse to see our nation as it is.

We began, after all, as a people who killed red men and enslaved black men. No doubt we often did this with a Bible and a prayer book. But no nation, however righteous its professions, could act as we did without burying deep in itself—in its customs, its institutions, and its psyche—a propensity toward violence. However much we pretended that Indians and Negroes were sub-human, we really knew that they were God's children too.

Nor did we confine our violence to red men and black men. We gained our freedom, after all, through revolution. The first century after independence were years of incessant violence—wars, slave insurrections, Indian fighting, urban riots, murders, duels, beatings. Members of Congress went armed to the Senate and House. In his first notable speech, in January 1838, before the Young Men's Lyceum of Springfield, Illinois, Abraham Lincoln named internal violence as the supreme threat to American political institutions. He spoke of "the increasing disregard for law which pervades the country; the growing disposition to substitute the wild and furious passions, in lieu of the sober judgment of Courts; and the worse than savage mobs, for the executive ministers of justice." The danger to the American republic, he said, was not from foreign invasion:

At what point then is the approach of danger to be expected? I answer, if it ever reach us, it must spring up amongst us. It cannot come from abroad. If destruction be our lot, we must ourselves be its author and finisher. As a nation of freemen, we must live through all time, or die by suicide.

So the young Lincoln named the American peril—a peril he did not fear to locate within the American breast. Indeed, the sadness of America has been that our worst qualities have so often been the other face of our best. Our commitment to morality, our faith in experiment:

these have been sources of America's greatness, but they have also led Americans into our error. For our moralists have sometimes condoned murder if the cause deemed good; so Emerson and Thoreau applauded John Brown of Osawatomie. And our pragmatists have sometimes ignored the means if the result is what they want. Moralism and pragmatism have not provided infallible restraints on the destructive instinct.

America, Martin Luther King correctly said, has been "a schizophrenic personality, tragically divided against herself." The impulses of violence and civility continued after Lincoln to war within the American breast. The insensate bloodshed of the Civil War exhausted the national capacity for violence and left the nation emotionally and psychologically spent. For nearly a century after Appomattox, we appeared on the surface the tranquil and friendly people we still like to imagine ourselves to be. The amiability of that society no doubt exerted a restraining influence. There were still crazy individuals, filled with grievance, bitterness, and a potential for violence. But most of these people expended their sickness in fantasy; the Guiteaus and the Czolgoszs were the exception. These years of stability, a stability fitfully recaptured after the First World War, created the older generation's image of a "normal" America.

Yet even in the kindly years we did not wholly eradicate the propensity toward violence which history had hidden in the national unconscious. In certain moods, indeed, we prided ourselves on our violence; we almost considered it evidence of our virility. "Above all," cried Theodore Roosevelt, "let us shrink from no strife, moral or physical, within or without the nation, provided we are certain that the strife is justified." That fatal susceptibility always lurked under the surface, breaking out in Indian wars and vigilantism in the West, in lynchings in the South, in labor riots and race riots and gang wars in the cities.

It is important to distinguish collective from individual violence—the work of mobs from the work of murderers; for the motive and the effect can be very different. There can, of course, be murder by a mob. But not all mobs aim at murder. Collective violence—rioting against what were considered illegal British taxes in Boston in 1773, or dangerous Papist influence sixty years later, or inequitable draft laws in New

York in 1863, or unfair labor practices in Chicago in 1937—is more characteristically directed at conditions than at individuals. In many cases (though by no means all), the aim has been to protest rather than protect the status quo; and the historian is obliged to concede that collective violence, including the recent riots in black ghettos, has often quickened the disposition of those in power to redress just grievances. Extra-legal group action, for better or worse, has been part of the process of American democracy. Violence, for better or worse, *does* settle some questions, and for the better. Violence secured American independence, freed the slaves, and stopped Hitler.

But this has ordinarily been the violence of a society. The individual who plans violence is less likely to be concerned with reforming conditions than with punishing persons. On occasion the purpose is to protect the status quo by destroying men who symbolize or threaten social change (a tactic which the anarchists soon began to employ in reverse). A difference exists in psychic color and content between spontaneous mass convulsions and the premeditated killing of individuals. The first signifies an unstable society, the second, a murderous society. America has exhibited both forms of violence.

Now in the third quarter of the twentieth century, violence has broken out with new ferocity in our country. What has given our old propensity new life? Why does the fabric of American civility no longer exert restraint? What now incites crazy individuals to act out their murderous dreams? What is it about the climate of this decade that suddenly encourages—that for some evidently legitimatizes—the relish for hate and the resort to violence? Why, according to the Federal Bureau of Investigation, have assaults with a gun increased 77 per cent in the four years from 1964 through 1967?

We talk about the legacy of the frontier. No doubt, the frontier has bequeathed us a set of romantic obsessions about six-shooters and gun fighters. But why should this legacy suddenly reassert itself in the 1960's?

We talk about the tensions of industrial society. No doubt the ever-quickening pace of social change depletes and destroys the institutions which make for social stability. But this does not explain why Americans shoot and kill so many more Americans than Englishmen kill Englishmen or Japanese kill Japanese. England, Japan and West Germany are, next to the United States, the most heavily industrialized countries in the world. Together they have a population of 214 million people. Among these 214 million, there are 135 gun murders a year. Among the 200 million people of the United States there are 6,500 gun murders a year—about *forty-eight times* as many.

We talk about the fears and antagonisms generated by racial conflict. Unquestionably this has contributed to the recent increase in violence. The murders of Dr. King and Senator Kennedy seem directly traceable to ethnic hatreds. Whites and black alike are laying in arms, both sides invoking the needs of self-defense. Yet this explanation still does not tell us why in America today we are tending to convert political problems into military problems—problems of adjustment into problems of force.

The New Left tells us that we are a violent society because we are a capitalist society—that capitalism is itself institutionalized violence; and that life under capitalism inevitably deforms relations among men. This view would be more impressive if the greatest violence of man against man in this century had not taken place in noncapitalist societies—in Nazi Germany, in Stalinist Russia, in precapitalist Indonesia. The fact is that every form of society is in some sense institutionalized violence; man in society always gives up a measure of "liberty" and accepts a measure of authority.

We cannot escape that easily. It is not just that we were a frontier society or are a racist or a capitalist society; it is something more specific than that. Nor can we blame the situation on our gun laws, or the lack of them; though here possibly we are getting closer. There is no question, of course, that we need adequate federal gun laws. Statistics make it evident that gun controls have some effect. Sixty per cent of all murders in the United States are by firearms; and states with adequate laws—New Jersey, New York, Massachusetts, Rhode Island—have much lower rates of gun murder than states with no laws or weak ones—Texas, Mississippi, Louisiana, Nevada.

Still, however useful in making it harder for potential murderers to get guns, federal gun legislation deals with the symptoms and not with the causes of our trouble. We must go further to account for the resurgence in recent years of our historical propensity toward violence.

One reason surely for the enormous tolerance of violence in contemporary America is the fact that our country has now been more or less continuously at war for a generation. The experience of war over a long period devalues human life and habituates people to killing. And the war in which we are presently engaged is far more brutalizing than was the Second World War or the Korean War. It is more brutalizing because the destruction we have wrought in Vietnam is so wildly out of proportion to any demonstrated involvement of our national security or any rational assessment of our national interest. In the other wars we killed for need. In this war we are killing beyond need, and, as we do so, we corrupt our national life. When violence is legally sanctioned for a cause in which people see no moral purpose, this is an obvious stimulus to individuals to use violence for what they may maniacally consider moral purposes of their own.

A second reason for the climate of violence in the United States is surely the zest with which the mass media, and especially television and films, dwell on violence. One must be clear about this. The mass media do *not* create violence. But they *reinforce* aggressive and destructive impulses, and they may well *teach* the morality as well as the methods of violence.

In recent years the movies and television have developed a pornography of violence far more demoralizing than the pornography of sex, which still seizes the primary attention of the guardians of civic virtue. Popular films of our day like *Rosemary's Baby* and *Bonnie and Clyde* imply a whole culture of human violation, psychological in one case, physical in the other. *Bonnie and Clyde*, indeed, was greatly admired for its blithe acceptance of the world of violence—an acceptance which almost became a celebration. Thus a student in a film course in San Francisco noted:

> *There is a certain spirit that belongs to us. We the American people. It is pragmatic, rebellious, violent, joyous. It can create or kill. Everything about* Bonnie and Clyde *captures this spirit.*
>
> *John Brown was motivated by this spirit and it has scared the hell out of historians ever since. The Black Panthers have it. Cab drivers, musicians, used car salesmen and bus drivers understand it, but doctors, dentists and real estate salesmen don't.*

Television is the most pervasive influence of all. The children of the electronic age sit hypnotized by the parade of killings, beatings, gunfights, knifings, maimings, brawls which flash incessantly across the tiny screen, and now in "living" color.

For a time, the television industry comforted itself with the theory that children listened to children's programs and that, if by any chance they saw programs for adults, violence would serve as a safety valve, offering a harmless outlet for pent-up aggressions: the more violence on the screen, the less in life. Alas, this turns out not to be necessarily so. As Dr. Wilbur Schramm, director of the Institute of Communication Research at Stanford, has reported, children, even in the early elementary school years, view more programs designed for adults than for themselves; "above all, they prefer the more violent type of adult program including the Western, the adventure program, and the crime drama." Experiments show that such programs, far from serving as safety valves for aggression, attract children with high levels of aggression and stimulate them to seek overt means of acting out their aggressions. Evidence suggests that these programs work the same incitement on adults. And televiolence does more than condition emotion and behavior. It also may attenuate people's sense of reality. Men murdered on the television screen ordinarily spring to life after the episode is over: all death is therefore diminished. A child asked a man last June where he was headed in his car. "To Washington," he said. "Why?" he asked. "To attend the funeral of Senator Kennedy." The child said, "Oh yeah—they shot him again." And such shooting may well condition the manner in which people approach the perplexities of existence. On television the hero too glibly resolves his problems by shooting somebody. The *Gunsmoke* ethos, however, is not necessarily the best way to deal with human or social complexity. It is hardly compatible with any kind of humane or libertarian democracy.

The problem of electronic violence raises difficult questions of prescription as well as of analysis. It would be fatal to restrain artistic exploration and portrayal, even of the most extreme and bitter aspects of human experience. No rational person wants to re-establish a reign of censorship or mobilize new Legions of Decency. Nor is there great gain in making the electronic media scapegoats for propensities which they reflect rather than create—propensities which spring from our history and our hearts.

Yet society retains a certain right of self-defense. Is it inconceivable that the television industry might work out forms of self-restraint? Beyond this, it should be noted that the networks and the stations do *not* own the airwaves; the nation does; and, if the industry cannot restrain itself, the Communications Act offers means, as yet unused, of democratic control.

We have a bad inheritance as far as violence is concerned; and in recent years war and television have given new vitality to the darkest strains in our national psyche. How can we master this horror in our souls before it rushes us on to ultimate disintegration?

There is not a problem of collective guilt, but there is a problem of collective responsibility. Certainly two hundred million Americans did not strike down John Kennedy or Martin Luther King or Robert Kennedy. But two hundred million Americans are plainly responsible for the character of a society that works on deranged men and incites them to depraved acts. There were Lee Harvey Oswalds and James Earl Rays and Sirhan Bishara Sirhans in America in the Thirties—angry, frustrated, alienated, resentful, marginal men in rootless, unstable cities like Dallas and Memphis and Los Angeles. But our society in the Thirties did not stimulate such men to compensate for their own failure by killing leaders the people loved.

Some of the young in their despair have come to feel that the answer to reason is unreason, the answer to violence, more violence; but these only hasten the plunge toward the abyss. The more intelligent disagree. They do not want America to beat its breast and go back to the golf course. *They do want America to recognize its responsibility.* They want us to tell it like it is—to confront the darkness in our past and the darkness in our present. They want us to realize that life is not solid and predictable but infinitely chancy, that violence is not the deviation but the ever-present possibility, that we can therefore never rest in the effort to prevent unreason from rending the skin of civility. They want our leaders to *talk* less about law and order and *do* more about justice.

Perhaps the old in American society might now learn that sanctimony is not a persuasive answer to anguish, and that we never cure ourselves if we deny the existence of a disease. If they learn this, if they face up to the schism in our national tradition, we all will have a better chance of subduing the impulse of destruction and of fulfilling the vision of Lincoln—that noble vision of a serene and decent society, united by bonds of affection and mystic chords of memory, dedicated at last to our highest ideals.

STUDY QUESTIONS

1. What is the author's thesis? Restate in your own words the problem he describes and the solutions he proposes.
2. The author states, "Even in the kindly years we did not wholly eradicate the propensity toward violence which history had hidden in the national unconscious." What do you think he means by the term "national unconscious"? Do you agree that our "propensity toward violence" is a result of our history, or would it rather be a result of the nature of man in general? Defend your answer.
3. What reasons does the author give for the increase in the tolerance for violence in our present-day society? Can you think of any additional or alternative reasons? Do you believe that all the reasons he lists are correct explanations?
4. Who were Guiteau and Czolgosz? Do you agree with the author that they were "exceptions" to the "tranquil, friendly people" of the post-Civil War period? Does the author consider Lee Oswald, James Earl Ray, or Sirhan Sirhan to be similar exceptions to the nature of our society today? Explain your answer.
5. Does the author pose any solutions to the situation he has described? Are they specific enough, in your opinion? What would you propose?

2

VIOLENCE AND MAN'S
STRUGGLE TO ADAPT*

Marshall F. Gilula and David N. Daniels

Dr. Gilula is resident in psychiatry and Dr. Daniels is assistant professor of psychiatry, Stanford University School of Medicine, Stanford, California. In this article Gilula and Daniels first define aggression and then raise the question of whether or not man is instinctively aggressive by presenting the three man series of aggression. Then they look at violence in America as represented by presidential assassinations, the presence of violence in mass media, the relation of mental illness and violence, and the relation of guns to violence. Finally they discuss whether it is possible to change the present condition of violence in America.

THE NEED is not really for more brains, the need is now for a gentler, a more tolerant people than those who won for us against the ice, the tiger, and the bear.[1]

Violence waits in the dusty sunlight of a tenement yard and in the shadows of a distraught mind. Violence draws nearer in the shouts of a protest march and in ghetto rumblings. Violence erupts from Mace-sprinkled billy clubs and a homemade Molotov cocktail. Violence of war explodes the peace it promises to bring. Hourly reports of violence bring numbness, shock, confusion, sorrow. We live in a violent world.[2]

Violence surrounds us, and we must try to understand it in the hopes of finding alternatives that will meet today's demand for change. Do we benefit from violence? Or is violence losing whatever adaptive value it may once have had? We present two theses. (i) Violence can

*"Violence and Man's Struggle to Adapt," Gilula, M.F. and Daniels, D.N. From *Science,* Vol. 164, pp. 396—405, 25 April 1969. Copyright 1969 by The American Association for the Advancement of Science.

best be understood in the context of adaptation. Violence is part of a struggle to resolve stressful and threatening events—a struggle to adapt. (ii) Adaptive alternatives to violence are needed in this technological era because the survival value of violent aggression is diminishing rapidly.

The shock of Robert F. Kennedy's death prompted the formation of a committee on violence[3] in the Department of Psychiatry, Stanford University School of Medicine. We committee members reviewed the literature on violence and then interpreted this literature from the point of view of psychiatrists and psychologists. We discussed our readings in seminars and sought answers to our questions about violence. This article presents a synthesis of our group's findings and observations and reflects our view of adaptation theory as a unifying principle in human behavior.

We define pertinent terms and describe the adaptation process before we examine violence as it relates to individual coping behavior and collective survival. We then describe three theories of aggression and relate them to adaptation. Next, we discuss relevant examples of violence as attempted coping behavior and factors that foster violence and illustrate the urgent need for other ways of expressing aggression. Finally, we consider the changing nature of adaptation and suggest ways of coping with violence.

Two groups of terms require definition: (i) aggression and violence; and (ii) adaptation, adjustment, and coping. We found that these terms have quite different meanings for different disciplines.

We here define aggression[4, 5] as the entire spectrum of assertive, intrusive, and attacking behaviors. Aggression thus includes both overt and covert attacks, such defamatory acts as sarcasm, self-directed attacks, and dominance behavior. We extend aggression to include such assertive behaviors as forceful and determined attempts to master a task or accomplish an act. We choose a broad definition of aggression rather than a restrictive one because relations between the underlying physiological mechanisms and the social correlates of dominant, assertive and violent behavior are still poorly understood. Hence, our definition encompasses but is broader than the definition of aggression in animals that is used in experimental biology,[6, 7] which says that an animal acts aggressively when he inflicts, attempts to inflict, or threatens to inflict damage upon another animal. Violence[4] is destructive aggression and involves inflicting physical damage on persons or property (since property is so often symbolically equated with the self). Violent inflicting of damage is often intense, uncontrolled, excessive, furious, sudden, or seemingly purposeless. Furthermore, violence may be collective or individual, intentional or unintentional, apparently just or unjust.

By adaptation we mean the behavioral and biological fit between the species and the environment resulting from the process of natural selection.[8, 9] In man, adaptation increasingly involves modifying the environment as well. Here we want to stress that behavior, especially group-living behavior in higher social species like man, is a crucial element in natural selection.[10] Adaptive behaviors are those that enhance species survival and, in most instances, individual survival. In contrast, we define adjustment as behavior of a group or individual that temporarily enhances the way we fit with the immediate situation. By definition, adjustment is often a passive rather than active process and does not result in an enduring alteration of behavior structure or patterns.[4, 11] In fact, adjustment may have biologically maladaptive consequences in the long run. In addition, rapid environmental change or extraordinary environmental circumstances may render formerly adaptive behaviors largely maladaptive,[10] that is, behaviors appropriate to past environmental conditions can work against survival in "new" or unusual environments.

We define coping as the continuing and usually successful struggle to accomplish tasks and goals with adaptive consequences. Put another way: "Behavior may be considered to serve coping functions when it increases the likelihood (from a specified vantage point with respect to a specified time unit) that a task will be accomplished according to standards that are tolerable both to the individual and to the group in which he lives".[12] Whereas each specific sequence of task-oriented behaviors may or may not have adaptive value, coping taken as a whole is an adaptive rather than adjustive human process.

Definition of Human Adaptations

Every culture prescribes the range of coping behaviors available to its people, but within this range individual adaptive behavior is forged and tested in times of stress. Stressful or new situations paradoxically offer us both the danger of failure and the opportunity for learning. Stress can be dangerous when it overwhelms the individual or group. Either the situation itself or unpleasant feelings about the situation (including massive anxiety) may block our usual resources and prevent problem solving, and aggressive reactions that are both indiscriminate and protective may occur. We may show primitive forms of behavior: passive adjustment, withdrawal, falsely blaming others, indiscriminate rage, violence, or confusion.

Alternately, stressful events provide a constructive challenge and expanded opportunity for learning. In a stressful situation that is not overwhelming, we seek information helpful in dealing with the situation and try to apply this information[13]. From information seeking and subsequent exploratory behavior come not only greater use of information and eventual mastery of new situations but also a sense of heightened self-awareness, enhanced coping skills, and personal growth.

A number of commonly occurring stressful life situations that may challenge and develop our coping skills have been recognized[13]. These are associated with the transitions in life and include adolescence, separation from parents, and marriage. Other challenging transitions involve cultural stresses, such as war and the threat of war; rapid technological change; and physical events, such as drought, earthquakes, and famine. These transition points in life are important because they provide opportunity for learning and developing more sophisticated ways of coping with problems.

We have marvelous adaptive abilities for coping with varying, even extreme, situations. These abilities result from cultural evolution interacting with our biological evolution. Culturally we survive through complex communal living. Through our living groups we obtain satisfaction, develop identity, and find meaning to life. Basic social values are of special cultural importance, for they determine the limits of acceptable behavior, expecially during times of stress. Biologically we are uniquely endowed for complex communal living. Such biological characteristics as aggression, the upright posture, prehension, speech, prolonged infancy and maturation, and profound development of the brain—all favor and allow for rich, dynamic, and complex living. Development of the cerebral hemispheres has played an especially important role in adaptation, for the cerebrum constitutes the biological basis of higher intelligence, self-awareness, complex language, and flexibility[8].

Thus through the interaction of biological evolution and cultural evolution, we have the equipment for adapting to and molding diverse environments. But this ability to adapt by manipulating the environment is now our cause for greatest concern, for in changing the environment, man changes the conditions necessary for his survival. We are now seeing an unprecedented acceleration of various man-made changes which call for accompanying changes in man, changes which we are having difficulty in making. While biological change is extremely slow, cultural change theoretically occurs at least every generation, although some aspects of culture (such as technology) change faster than others (for example, beliefs and customs). The term "generation gap" not only describes how we today view the battle of the generations but also alludes to the speed of cultural change and how people have trouble keeping pace. Living in the electronic age, we watch televised accounts of pre-agricultural-age violence and feel our industrial-age mentality straining to cope with the environment.

Since survival results from the long-range adaptiveness of our behavior, knowledge of adaptive mechanisms is important for understanding the role of violence in human behavior and survival. In the section that follows we shall relate three theories of aggression to adaptation.

Adaptation and Theories of Aggression

Aggression has helped man survive. Aggression in man—including behaviors that are assertive, intrusive, and dominant as well as violent—is fundamental and adaptive. Violence is not a result of aggression but simply a form of aggression. Nor is all violence necessarily motivated by destructive aggression. For instance, in the sadistic behavior of sexual assaults, violence is evoked in part by sexual motives. In other instances, violence can occur accidentally or without conscious intent, as in many auto accidents. Currently there are three main views of aggression—all involving adaptation—but each suggests a different solution to the problem of violent behavior. Broadly labeled, these theories are (i) the biological-instinctual theory, (ii) the frustration theory, and (iii) the social-learning theory.

1) *The biological-instinctual theory*[14-16] holds that aggressive behavior, including violence, is an intrinsic component of man resulting from natural selection: Man is naturally aggressive. It is hard to imagine the survival of man without aggressiveness, namely because aggression is an element of all purposeful behavior and, in many cases, provides the drive for a particular action. This theory says that aggression includes a wide variety of behaviors, many of which are constructive and essential

to an active existence. Stimulus-seeking behavior (for example, curiousity or the need to have something happen) is certainly at least as important a facet of human behavior as avoidance behavior and need-satisfaction. Seeking the novel and unexpected provides much of life's color and excitement. Aggression can supply much of the force and power for man's creative potential.

Psychiatric and psychoanalytic case studies are one source of evidence supporting this theory[14-17]. Examples range from individuals with destructive antisocial behavior who express violent aggression directly and often impulsively, to cases of depression and suicide in which violent aggression is turned against the self, and to seriously inhibited persons for whom the expression of aggression, even in the form of assertion, is blocked almost entirely. Psychiatrists and other mental-health professionals describe many disordered behaviors as stemming from ramifications and distortions of the aggressive drive[14].

Animal studies [6, 15, 18] (including primate field studies), studies of brain-damaged humans, and male-female comparisons provide behavioral, anatomical, and hormonal data illustrating the human predisposition to aggression. Among nonhuman mammals, intraspecies violence occurs less frequently than with humans[7]. When violent aggressive behaviors do occur among members of the same species, they serve the valuable functions of spacing the population over the available land and maintaining a dominance order among the group members. Uncontrolled aggression in animals generally occurs only under conditions of overcrowding. Aggression in humans, even in the form of violence, has had similar adaptive value historically.

The biological-instinctual theory suggests that since aggression is inevitable, effective controls upon its expression are necessary, and reduction of violence depends upon providing constructive channels for expressing aggression.

2) *The frustration theory*[19] states that aggressive behavior comes from interfering with ongoing purposeful activity. A person feels frustrated when a violation of his hopes or expectations occurs, and he then tries to solve the problem by behaving aggressively. Frustrations can take various forms: threats to life, thwarting of basic needs, and personal insults. This theory often equates aggression with destructive or damaging violent behavior. Major factors influencing aggressive responses to frustration are the nature of the frustration, previous experi-

ence, available alternatives for reaction (aggression is by no means the only response to frustration), the person's maturity, and the preceding events or feelings. Even boredom may provoke an aggressive response. As a response to frustration, aggression is often viewed as a learned rather than an innate behavior. According to this theory, frustration-evoked aggression aims at removing obstacles to our goals; hence the frustration theory also ties in with adaptation. The aggressive response to frustration often is a form of coping behavior that may have not only adjustive but also long-range consequences.

The frustration theory suggests that control or reduction of violence requires reducing existing frustrations as well as encouraging constructive redirection of aggressive responses to frustration. This reduction includes removing or improving frustrating environmental factors that stand between personal needs and environmental demands. Such factors include violation of human rights, economic deprivation, and various social stresses.

3) *The social-learning theory*[20] states that aggressive behavior results from child-rearing practices and other forms of socialization. Documentation comes from sociological and anthropological studies and from observing social learning in children. Aggressive behavior can be acquired merely by watching and learning—often by imitation—and does not require frustration. Aggressive behaviors rewarded by a particular culture or subculture usually reflect the basic values and adaptive behaviors of the group. In American culture, where achievement, self-reliance, and individual self-interest are valued highly, we also find a relatively high emphasis on military glory, a relatively high incidence of personal crime, and a society characterized by a relatively high degree of bellicosity. Similar patterns occur in other cultures. From this theory we infer that as long as a nation values and accepts violence as an effective coping strategy, violent behavior will continue.

The social-learning theory of aggression suggests that control and reduction of violence require changes in cultural traditions, child-rearing practices, and parental examples. Parents who violently punish children for violent acts are teaching their children how and in what circumstances violence can be performed with impunity. Other changes in cultural traditions would emphasize prevention rather than punishment of violent acts and, equally important, would emphasize human rights and group effort rather than excessive and isolated self-reliance.

The first step toward making the changes that will reduce violence is to examine our values. We must decide which values foster violence and then begin the difficult job of altering basic values.

In reality, the three theories of aggression are interrelated. Proclivities for social learning and for frustration often have a biological determinant. For example, the biology of sex influences the learning of courting behavior. Regarding violence, from these theories of aggression we see that the many expressions of violence include man's inherent aggression, aggressive responses to thwarted goals, and behavior patterns imitatively learned within the cultural setting. All three theories of aggression and violence fit into the adaptation-coping explanation. Violence is an attempt to cope with stressful situations and to resolve intolerable conflicts. Violence may have short-run adjustive value, even when the long-run adaptive consequences may in fact be adverse. It is the sometimes conflicting natures of adjustment and adaptation that are confusing and insufficiently appreciated. In some instances violence emerges when other more constructive coping strategies have failed. In other instances violence is used to enhance survival. Our species apparently has overabsorbed violence into our cultures as a survival technique. Children and adolescents have learned well the accepted violent behaviors of their elders.

All three theories help us understand violent behavior and hence suggest potential ways of reducing violence. In the following sections we consider current examples of violence from the perspective of those factors in our society that foster violence and from the standpoint of how these examples reflect the changing nature of adaptation.

Phenomenon of Presidential Assassination

Assassination is not an isolated historical quirk, eluding comprehension or analysis. The event is usually overdetermined by multiple but equally important factors: personal qualities of the assassin, a fatalistic posture assumed by the victim, and such factors in the social environment as political stereotypes, murder sanctions, and the symbolic nature of high offices.

Although assassination can strike down anyone, we have restricted our examination to assassination of presidents in America[21] by studying the personal qualities of "successful" assassins and of others who almost succeeded. Of the eight assassination attempts on American presidents, four have been successful. The following facts emerge. (i) All the assassination attempts were made with guns, all but one with pistols. (ii) All the assassins were shorter and weighed less than average men of the period. (iii) All the assassins were young adult Caucasian males. (iv) All the assassination attempts but one were made by individuals who were seriously disturbed or even paranoid schizophrenics.[22] The exception was the final attempt of two Puerto Rican nationalists to kill President Harry S. Truman. The successful assassins, for the most part, were mentally unbalanced and had persecutory and grandiose delusions.

Assassination provides a method for instantly satisfying a need for personal importance. The delusional assassin very probably had a fantasy that once the act was committed, an outcry of favorable opinion and acclaim would vindicate what he had done. In most of the instances of attempted or successful assassination, escape plans were inadequate or nonexistent.

The life pattern of most of the assassins included extreme resentment toward others—a resentment aggravated by a long history of isolation and loneliness. Often the isolation stemmed from poor and inconsistent relations with parents and others early in life, which resulted in most of the assassins having resentment and mistrust of parental figures. Their resentment toward parental figures might have included the President (political symbol of parenthood) as the head of the federal government. In response to imagined unfair treatment from others and a distortion of his own inadequacies, the assassin turned his anger on the chief of state.

Typically the assassin had struggled for importance, success, and manliness, but had failed. At the time of the attempted presidential assassination, the assassin was on a downward life course. Haunted by resentment and failure and plagued with disordered thinking and distortions of reality, the assassin took action. Shooting the President was thus an attempt to resolve conflicts with which he apparently could not otherwise cope. Providing an alternate outlet for his violent dissatisfaction would be one way of preventing the potential assassin from killing. Perhaps the ombudsman (public complaint receiver) system would allow the would-be assassin to voice his grievances against his intended victim, thereby lessening his pent-up frustrations and reducing the likelihood that he would kill.

Our discussion of another important determinant of assassination—the victim's fatalistic attitude—is not restricted to presidential assassinations. The fatalistic thinking and actions of several assassination victims are reflected in their strong disinclination toward taking precautionary measures despite recognizing the existence of violent impulses in others toward presidents and presidential candidates. Robert Kennedy stated a view that he shared with Abraham Lincoln, Martin Luther King, Jr., and John F. Kennedy: "There's no sense in worrying about those things. If they want you, they can get you."[23] This attitude often leads to dangerous negligence that is an exaggerated form of denying that one is actually afraid of physical harm. Lincoln has been described as "downright reckless"[24] about personal safety. Robert Kennedy was quoted as saying, "I'll tell you one thing: If I'm President, you won't find me riding around in any of those awful [bullet-proof] cars."[23] The fatalistic attitude illustrated by statements like this is encouraged by our tradition of expecting physical courage in our leaders. Men who repeatedly and publicly proclaim their vulnerability may be unwittingly encouraging assassination by offering an invitation to the delusional, grandiose, and isolated person who dreams of accomplishing at least one important and publicly recognized act in his life. "Mixing with the people" is firmly embedded in the American political tradition, but it is also an accomplice to assassination. One way to cope with this problem would be legislation to restrict the contact and exposure of a President with crowds when his presence has been announced in advance.

Mass Media and Violence

Television could be one of our most powerful tools for dealing with today's violence. It could provide education and encourage, if not induce, desired culture modification. Unfortunately, it does little of either today, perhaps because the harmful effects of televised violence have been glossed over. However, all the mass media do little to discourage and much to encourage violence in America. The Ugly American as a national stereotype is rapidly being displaced in the eyes of the world by the Violent American, his brother of late. This stereotype is fostered by the media but is sustained by the violent acts of some of our citizens. Armed with shotgun, ignorance, frustrations, or hunger, this Violent American can be seen today throughout our society. We are not all violent Americans, but mass media are giving us the violence we seem to want.

What effect do the mass media have?[25] All of us are probably affected by the media to some degree, but most research has focused on children, since an immature and developing mind is usually less capable of discrimination when responding to a given stimulus. One comprehensive review[26] described short-term effects that include the child's emotional reactions to what he views, reads, and hears. Long-term effects, what the child actually learns as a result of his exposure, may include vocabulary, factual information, belief systems, and such altered personality characteristics as increased aggressiveness. No one selects all 'the media materials available, nor does anyone absorb or retain the selected materials consistently or completely. Prior information, differing needs, and quality of life adjustment also help to filter the child's processing of the offered materials. Mass media effects also depend somewhat on the applicability of the learned material to the child's own life situation.

Similarly, as shown by another researcher,[27] frustration, the anger evoked by it, the overall situation, the apparent severity and justification of the violence viewed in a film—all relate to whether or not children use these aggressive responses.

A large study in Great Britain[28] showed that certain portrayals of violence are more disturbing to children than others. Unusual motives, settings, and weapons are more disturbing than stereotyped violence. For example, knives or daggers are more upsetting than guns or fist fights. Similarly, seeing violence or disasters in newsreels bothered children more than dramatized violence.

Another study[29] found that the average American child from 3 through 16 years old spends more of his waking hours watching television than attending school. First-graders spend 40 percent and sixth-graders spend 80 percent of their viewing time watching "adult" programs, with Westerns and situation comedies being most popular. By the eighth grade, children favor crime programs.

Can we justifiably say that the media teach violence? Television teaches more than vocabulary and factual information to the impressionable young viewer, who learns by identification and social imitation. Learning theorists have shown that children readily mimic the aggressive behavior of adults and that the degree of imitation is comparable whether the behavior is live or televised. In another study[30] nursery school children watched a film of adults aggressively hitting an inflatable plastic figure, a Bobo doll. Later these and other children were first mildly frustrated and then led individually into a room in which they found the Bobo doll and other materials not shown in the film. Those who had seen the film imitated precisely the film's physical and verbal aggression and made more aggressive use of other toys, such as guns, that had not been in the film. Film-watchers showed twice as much aggressiveness as those who had not seen the film.

These children were all from a "normal" nursery school population, and all showed some effect. This finding seriously questions the claim that such violence is learned only by deviant individuals. The findings apply equally to real, fictional, and fantasy violence. The impact on children observing aggressive behavior has been further corroborated in experiments in which live models, cartoons, and play materials were used. The idea that watching television satisfactorily releases pent-up aggressions (the catharsis theory) loses credibility in the face of these data from social-learning experiments. Watching dramatized violence may actually lead to subsequent aggressive behavior.

A tendency toward repeating certain behaviors viewed in the media clearly exists. The mass media teach the alphabet of violence, but whether or not the actual performance of violent behaviors occurs depends on personality, subcultural values, and other factors. The research to date indicates that the learning of violence must be distinguished from the performance of it. One fear we have is that restraints and taboos against violent behavior may diminish as the result of observing prohibited behavior being condoned and rewarded on the screen. Violence depicts a way of life; it is disguised by a cloak of history or locale and becomes acceptable. We are never taught "in this School for Violence that violence in itself is something reprehensible."[31]

Even with the portrayed violence, the screen environment may be more desirable than the viewer's actual environment. In the culturally deprived American household the underfed, underoccupied, under-educated person may be an apt pupil of the school for violence. Such pupils more readily accept as real a violent world made of movies, newsprint, comic books, and video. The blurred line between fiction and reality grows fainter when there is nothing for dinner. Ghetto violence is one way of at least temporarily adjusting to intolerable personal frustrations and an unbearable environment.

Given the effectiveness of the mass media in achieving culture modification, we should determine whether the content of the media produces desirable or undesirable modification. How frequently is violent content offered in our media? According to a 1951 New Zealand study,[32] 70 American films had roughly twice as much violence per film as did 30 films from other countries. A 1954 study of network television programs[33] found an actual doubling from one year to the next in the number of acts or threats of violence, with much of the increase occurring during children's viewing hours. These studies were all conducted before the documentary and news depiction of violence became common, and thus these studies dealt essentially with fictional violence. More recent studies reflect the same trends, however. A New York *Times* headline from July 1968, reads "85 Killings Shown in 85½ TV Hours on the 3 Networks."[34]

Thus the media's repetitive, staccato beat of violence and the evidence of its impact upon the most impressionable members of our society show that violence is valued, wanted, enjoyed. In teaching that violence is a good quick way to get things done, television and other media teach that violence is adaptive behavior.

Part of the tragedy is that the mass media could effectively promote adaptive behaviors like nonviolent protest and other alternatives to violence. The communications personnel and we consumers alike share the responsibility for seeing that our mass media develop their own constructive educational potential. At the very least, violence in the media must be reduced. The statement is hackneyed, the conclusion is not.

Mental Illness, Violence, and Homicide

What is the relationship between mental illness and violence?[35] Generally the stereotype of the mentally ill person as a potentially dangerous criminal is not valid. The act of homicide often raises the question of psychosis, but only a relatively few psychotic individuals are potential murderers. The stereotype is kept alive, however, by the sensationalist news coverage of the few homicides committed by psychotics.

Mental illness does not usually predispose one to commit violent acts toward others. The patient with severe mental illness (psychosis) is frequently so preoccupied with himself and so disorganized that he is more likely to commit suicide than homicide. A main exception is the fairly well-organized paranoid patient with persecutory delusions concerning one or more particular individuals, intense hostility and mistrust for others, and a pervasive tendency to blame his troubles on the world. However, this type of mentally disordered person constitutes a small minority and does not greatly increase the low incidence of violent acts committed by those identified as mentally ill. In fact, several comparative studies indicate that patients discharged from mental hospitals have an arrest rate considerably lower than that of the general population. In a Connecticut state mental hospital[36] the felony arrest rate was 4.2 per 1000 patients, whereas among the general population it was 27 per 1000. Compared to an arrest rate of 491 per 100,000 among the general population, New York state mental hospitals[37] reported a figure of 122 per 100,000 for male patients discharged during 1947. Ten thousand patients were studied. One statewide survey of Maryland psychiatric hospitals[38] showed that the mentally ill are involved in criminal behavior about as often as the general population.

Since mental illness of itself is not predictive of violence or homicide, we must look for other predisposing conditions. Predicting specifically who will murder is difficult because over 90 percent of the murders committed are not premeditated and 80 percent involve an acquaintance or family member.[39] One often demonstrated factor related to homicide is the excessive use of alcohol.[40] Overindulgence in alcohol has been cited as one feature of the "pre-assaultive state".[40] Persons who are preassaultive usually show some combination of the following five factors: (i) difficulty enjoying leisure time often associated with the heavy use of alcohol; (ii) frequent clashes with close friends, spouse, and others; (iii) history of many fistfights and evidence of past violence (such as scars) reflecting difficulty with impulse control; (iv) fondness for guns and knives; and (v) being relatively young, usually under 45 years old. Comparing homicide rates for males and females universally indicates that a potential murderer is more often male than female. This difference reflects more frequent use of guns and knives ("male" weapons) for murdering as well as sex differences in expressing aggression.

Case histories of homicide reveal repeatedly that a person uses murder as a means of conflict resolution in an unbearable situation for which he can find no other solution. Predisposing factors for homicide include alcoholism, subcultural norms accepting violence as a means of settling conflict, a setting in which the individual experiences intolerable frustration or attack, helplessness resulting from the unavailability of or the inability to perceive alternative actions, intense emotions, and distortion of reality (perhaps even to the point where reality disappears because of personality disintegration). In the instance of blind rage, a person sometimes murders without realizing what he is doing.

The act of homicide may be viewed as attempted coping behavior. Homicide eliminates the immediate problem at a time when there seems to be no future or when the future seems unimportant, and the long-range consequences of the act are not considered. Put another way, homicide has adjustive rather than adaptive value.

Firearms Control and Violence

Violence by firearms has recently caused great concern.[41, 42] The question of whether there is a gun problem is complicated by regional variations in both the actual incidence and the reporting of crime and multiple psychosocial variables, such as individual "choice" of homicide, population density, age, race, socioeconomic status, religion, and law-enforcement effectiveness.

Even so, the following statistics[39, 43] estimating the involvement of guns in various forms of violence in America indicate that a problem does exist. In 1967 firearms caused approximately 21,500 deaths— approximately 7,700 murders, 11,000 suicides, and 2,800 accidental deaths. In addition, there were also about 55,000 cases of aggravated assault by gun and 71,000 cases of armed robbery by gun. Between 1960 and 1967, firearms were used in 96 percent (that is, 394) of 411 murders of police officers. More than 100,000 nonfatal injuries were caused by firearms during 1966. A study in Chicago[44] in which assaults with guns were compared to those with knives shows many more equally serious assaults with knives than with guns; but more of the gun assaults were fatal. Another study[27] convincingly shows that the mere presence of a gun serves as a stimulus to aggression, that is, "The finger pulls the trigger, but the trigger may also be pulling the finger." The number of guns owned by citizens is unknown, but estimates run from 50 to 200 million.[39] In 1967 approximately 4,585,000 firearms were sold in the United States, of which 1,208,000 were imports.[43] Lately, data from a 1963 World Health Organization survey of 16 developed countries[39] give America an overwhelming lead in death rates for both homicide and suicide by firearms.

These data speak for themselves. What they do not show are the steady increases in all categories for gun-related mortality cited during the past few years. Firearms sales increased by 132 percent between 1963 and 1967.

Responsibility for legal restrictions on guns has generally been left to the states. Consequently, regulations on the sale of guns vary greatly. The lack of uniform laws and the ability (until recently) to buy guns in one state and transport them to another state have made it difficult to compare accurately the gun laws of different states. Even the so-called strict gun laws may not possess sufficient strength to reduce gun killings significantly.

Until 1968 there were only two federal laws of note.[45] The National Firearms Act of 1934 imposes a tax on the transfer of certain fully automatic weapons and sawed-off shotguns. The Federal Firearms Act of 1938 requires a license for interstate sale of firearms and prohibits interstate shipment of guns to convicted felons, fugitives, and certain other persons. Two bills passed in 1968 go somewhat further but do not include firearm registration.[41] The Omnibus Crime Control and Safe Streets Act restricts interstate and foreign commerce in hand guns. The Gun Control Act also adds mail-order sale of rifles and shotguns to this restriction and prohibits over-the-counter sales to out-of-state residents, juveniles, convicted felons, drug users, mental defectives, and patients committed to mental hospitals.

Although the data do not provide an ironclad indictment against weak, inconsistent legislation, we believe that they make a convincing argument. What is more, more than two-thirds of the American people continue to favor stronger gun-control legislation.[42] Even the frightening regularity of assassination has not resulted in strong legislation (that is, legislation requiring registration of guns and owners). How then can we account for the successful opposition to strong gun legislation?

Diverse groups comprise the one-third or less of Americans who do not favor stricter gun control laws. The most visible opposition group is the large (about 1 million members), well-organized National Rifle Association (NRA). With an immense operating budget (approximately $5.7 million in 1967), the NRA is an especially effective "gun lobby".[46] Another group, the Black Panthers, sees arms as necessary for survival. Eldridge Cleaver, Defense Minister of the Black Panthers, wrote, "We are going to keep our guns to protect ourselves from the pigs [police]."[47] Protection is also the issue in Dearborn, Michigan, where housewives are arming against the potential rioter and looter who might "invade" Dearborn from Detroit. Tragic escalation continues around the interplay or urban and suburban action and reaction.

Arguments opposing gun legislation can be divided into five overlapping categories.

1) Gun control would cause the loss of rights and possessions. This argument takes various forms: Restrictive legislation is an effort to disarm American sportsmen and law-abiding citizens; legislation would result in the loss of the so-called basic American freedom, "the right of the people to keep and bear arms"; and maintaining an armed citizenry ensures the protection of American liberties, especially against tyrannies from the political right or left. A common fear is that gun laws could lead from registration to discrimination and finally to confiscation of all firearms.

Our traditional frontier and rural ways of life are disappearing, and with this change has come a decrease in our traditional freedom and individualism. For many opposing gun legislation, the actual and potential loss of a way of life and its prized symbol—the gun—make gun legislation a concern basic to the adaptiveness of our society. These opponents assume that restrictions on the "right to bear arms" endanger our way of life.

2) Guns represent protection from dangers. The gun is seen as providing personal protection from and a means of coping with life-threatening dangers and destructive evil forces, be they criminals, drug addicts, rapists, communists, other subversives, mental patients, rioters, police, or racists. The NRA promotes this coping strategy in its official publication, *The American Rifleman.*[48] A monthly NRA column, "The Armed Citizen," states that "law-enforcement officers cannot at all times be where they are needed to protect life or property in danger of serious violation. In many such instances, the citizen has no choice but to defend himself with a gun."[48] The power of this argument depends upon a person's feelings of helplessness and mistrust in the face of danger.

Many people in urban areas or changing neighborhoods fear the rising crime rate and the breakdown of law and order. However, there is no documentation that an armed citizenry provides greater individual or group protection than an unarmed citizenry. On the contrary, the potential danger of such individual armed protection in our congested urban society includes harm to innocent bystanders, accidental shootings, and the increased likelihood of impulsive violence, which already accounts for over 90 percent of homicides in America.

3) Crime is reduced by punishment and not by gun control. Several forms of this argument state that gun-control legislation simply is not an effective way of reducing crime and violence: (i) Guns don't kill people, people kill people; (ii) when guns are outlawed, only outlaws will have guns (because they steal them anyway); (iii) crime is not associated with guns but with such social factors as population density, population composition, economic status, and strength of police; and (iv) effective enforcement of present laws has not been tried.

Using stronger and even cruel punishment to cope with gun-using criminals has to date not been proven as an effective deterrent, and its use, we believe, is morally indefensible. The "crime and punishment" thesis ignores data showing that more than three out of four homicides and two out of three criminal assaults occur among family and friends, that is, most murders are committed by "law-abiding citizens." In addition, criminals can and do purchase weapons from legal sources.

4) A gun represents strength and manliness. Gun literature usually implies this argument. Acts of heroism and bravery are associated with gun usage. Members of the NRA receive distinguished fighting medals. Pictures and advertisements reflect manliness and imply that gun usage means "standing up for your rights."

Guns may serve as a source of power, pride, and independence (the "equalizer"—for feelings of inferiority or inadequacy) and as the symbol of manliness and potency. Guns can and do represent these qualities in our culture, even to a pathological degree for some of us.

5) Guns provide recreation and support the economy. Arguments here portray citizens as being restricted from and deprived of healthy outdoor life, the hobby of gun collecting, family recreation, and the fellowship associated with hunting and target shooting. For example, an article in *The American Rifleman* entitled "Happiness is a Warm Gun"[49] depicts a close father-son relationship based on shooting. Additionally, gun sales and fees are held to be important economic factors supporting hunting states and conservation programs.

These arguments indicate that the issue of gun legislation is pragmatic, ideological, psychological, and economic, and is not based upon sound empirical data. The fervor of the arguments accurately reflects the deep emotional attachments at stake. Indeed, the specific content of proposed gun laws often seems irrelevant. Tragically, the arguments confuse ideology with issues of violence that must be solved. If strictly pragmatic issues of protection were involved, better police protection and increased communication with the feared group or groups should diminish the fear.

Finally, we have found that the "statistics game" is often played by both sides of this particular controversy. By presenting selected statistics and invalid inferences, both sides have obscured the more important goals of reducing gun killings and violence.

Yet, on balance, data document the need for strong and more uniform firearms legislation. We know of no single issue concerning violence that reflects more clearly the changing nature of adaptation. Challenges of the complex urban society in which we live cannot be met with old frontier means of survival—every man protecting himself with his own gun. Yet, gun legislation is no panacea. While reflecting America's desire for action, focusing or relying on legislation alone tends to obscure basic issues of violence and how we persist in using both individual and collective violence as a means of resolving conflict.

Collective and Sanctioned Violence

An additional dilemma is that killing is neither legally nor socially defined as an unequivocally criminal act. The existence of capital punishment and war gives qualified sanction to violence as a means of resolving conflict. Both the general public and their leaders always seem to be able to justify any violence perpetrated on their fellow man. Thus in practice the legitimacy of violence is arbitrary and depends more on the will of powerful men than on moral, ethical, or humane considerations. In a sense, all sanctioned violence is collective, since it has group social approval. Certainly the existence of sanctioned violence abrades the concept of law and order.

We desperately need research on the psychological processes that permit an individual or group to view some violence as good (and presumably adaptive) and other forms of violence as bad (and presumably maladaptive). Although the history of violence in man is polymorphous, there likely are psychological mechanisms common to all cultures and times. For instance, the psychology of sanctioned violence everywhere depends on attributing evil motives to the "outsiders." Then because "they" are violent (evil), "we" *have* to be violent, or (twisted even further) because "they" are violent, it is *good* for "us" to be violent.

Thus people who have seen sanctioned violence being committed in the name of law, order, justice, moral obligation and duty come to use violence themselves as a "just" means of solving their own problems. The people are acting as their government's representatives have acted— if the cause is just, the grievance real, then unlimited power and force can be used.

Nowhere do we better find this thinking reflected than in the actions of rioters.[50] Study of the 1967 Detroit uprising[51] showed that the rioters (young, better educated men who had experienced frustration of their rising expectations) viewed violence against the "system" as justified. Not surprisingly, their views of what justifies violence differed greatly from those of the law enforcers and of the middle-aged black citizens. To the rioters violence was a means of accomplishing goals seemingly not attainable by nonviolent means. Their belief in the power of violence is understandable. Civil disorders are serving in part as a catalyst for change and an instrument of achievement. Some uprising participants reported that violence provided a sense of manliness and strength. But do these supposed gains outweigh the damage of escalations of counterviolence and potential suppression? At least the hypothesis that violence purifies and enhances manliness, and strengthens identity is subject to empirical study.

The results of social-psychiatric field investigations like those in Detroit and in Brandeis University's Lemberg Center for the Study of Violence are useful steps toward understanding the psychological processes and conditions evoking collective violence. For instance, a Lemberg report[52] cited four socio-psychological antecedents to ghetto uprisings: (i) a severe conflict of values between dominant and minority groups; (ii) a "hostile belief system" held by the aggrieved group, based considerably on reality; (iii) a failure of communication between the aggrieved and dominant groups; and (iv) a failure in social control resulting from either overcontrol or undercontrol. In short, these studies show that psychiatrists and psychologists can and must help to resolve the crisis of violence through field studies, facilitating communication between opposing groups, and making recommendations for social change.

But what of war? Behavioral scientists have grasped at all sorts of explanations for this species' warring behavior. Perhaps even this attempt to explain war is a cause of war; our ability to justify any form of violence is part of man's magnificent cerebral endowment. Many causes of war have been suggested: contiguity, habituation, social learning, predation, psychological defenses (for example, rationalization, blaming, denial, counterphobic tendencies among others), the host of fears associated with the human condition, territoriality and power, intolerable frustration, biologically rooted aggressive instincts, and sadism.[53-55] One wonders whether the mere distance and speed with which we kill are factors rendering meaningless the signals of submission that other animals use to halt violent encounters.[54] Often we literally no longer have to touch the results of our violence. The impersonal factor shows up in another way. Since war is an activity between organized nation states rather than angry individuals, decisions producing war often are made in a calculated manner by those who do not participate directly in any personal acts of violence.

The evidence of history is that war proves everything and nothing. An adequate analysis of the Vietnam war and of the myriad of other wars dotting history is far too great a task for this discussion, despite the relevance of war to the current crisis of violence.[55]

Although preventive measures are difficult to administer in the face of the contradicting sanctioned and unsanctioned violence, there are remedies to violence, and we have discussed some of them. More effort could be expended trying to understand the all-important relation between the excessive use of alcohol and homicide. Disseminating currently available information on how to identify a potential murderer will help. Despite Americans' conflicting feelings about guns, there is a gun-death problem today, and more effective and uniform gun legislation can keep guns out of the hands of those who are likely to act impulsively. The mass media can play an increasingly responsible and educational role, while reducing the amount of violence for violence's sake. Many positive potentials of the media have not yet been tapped. Citizen complaint agencies can be established, of which one possibility might be homicide prevention centers along the lines of the suicide prevention centers. Frustrated minority groups will become less frustrated when

they are not blocked from responsible participation and self-determina-
tion. Peaceful resolution of conflict[56] such as nonviolent protest and
negotiation, reducing the amount of sanctioned violence, encouraging a
shared sense of humanity, and moving toward rehabilitation rather than
retribution in dealing with crime—all these are promising directions.
Violence must be studied scientifically so that human behavior can be
sustained by knowledge.

Changing Nature of Human Adaptation:
Some Speculations

Violence is unique to no particular region, nation, or time.[55] Centuries ago man survived primarily as a nomadic hunter relying on
violent aggression for both food and protection. Even when becoming
agricultural and sedentary, man struggled against nature, and survival
still required violent aggression, especially for maintaining territory
when food was scarce.

Then in a moment of evolution man's energies suddenly produced
the age of technology. Instead of adapting mainly by way of biological evolution, we are now increasingly subject to the effects and
demands of cultural evolution. Instead of having to adapt to our environment, we now can adapt our environment to our needs. Despite this
potential emancipation from biological evolution, we retain the adaptive mechanisms derived from a long history of mammalian and primate
evolution, including our primitive forms of aggression, our violence,
bellicosity, and inclination to fight in a time of emergency. Where these
mechanisms once responded more to physical stress, they now must
respond more to social, cultural, and psychological stresses, and the
response does not always produce adaptive results. Where violent aggressive behavior once served to maintain the human species in times of
danger, it now threatens our continued existence.

In this new era, culture changes so rapidly that even time has assumed another dimension—the dimension of acceleration. Looking to
the past becomes less relevant for discerning the future.

In the current rapidly expanding technological era, many once useful modes of adaptation are transformed into threats to survival. Territorial exclusivity is becoming obsolete in an economy of abundance.
Vast weapons, communication, and transportation networks shrink the
world to living-room size and expand our own backyard to encompass a

"global village." Yet war and exclusivity continue. Our exploitation of natural resources becomes maladaptive. Unlimited reproduction, once adaptive for advancing the survival of the species, now produces the over-crowded conditions similar to those that lead to destructive and violent behavior in laboratory experiments with other species.

The rate at which we change our environment now apparently exceeds our capacity for adapting to the changes we make. Technological advances alter our physical and social environments, which in turn demand different adaptive strategies and a reshaping of culture. The accelerated civilization of technology is crowded, complex, ambiguous, uncertain. To cope with it, we must become capable of restructuring knowledge of our current situation and then applying new information adaptively. Several factors give us reason to hope that we can succeed.

1) Our social organization and intellectual abilities give us vast potential for coping. Knowledge and technology can be harnessed to serve goals determined by man. Automation makes possible the economics of abundance, but only our cultural values can make abundance a reality for all people. Medicine permits us to control life, but we have not yet seen fit to use this power to determine the limits of population. The technologies of communication and travel shrink the world, but man has not yet expanded the horizon of exclusion. We can learn to unite in goals that transcend exclusivity and direct cultural evolution in accordance with adaptive values and wisdom. The past need not be master of our future.

2) Violence can be understood and controlled. The crisis is one of violence, not of aggression, and it is violence that we must replace. Aggression in the service of adaptation can build and create rather than destroy. The several theories of aggression and current issues of violence suggest many complementary ways of controlling and redirecting aggression. We have suggested some in this article. Furthermore, our brief review of theory and issues points to many possibilities for multidimensional research—an approach that we believe is needed rather than "one note" studies or presentations.

3) Greater attention can be focused on both social change and adaptation processes. Cultural lag in the technological era produces not stability but a repetitious game of "catch up" characterized by one major social crisis after another and by behaviors that are too often only adjustive in that they bring relief of immediate problems while

doing little to provide long-range solutions. Expanding our knowledge of the processes of social change and understanding resistance to change are of highest priority. Unforeseen change produces intolerable stress, anxiety, and increased resistance to rational change. These reactions inhibit solution-seeking behavior; evoke feelings of mistrust, loss, and helplessness; and lead to attacks on the apparent agents of change. We must develop the ability to foresee crises and actively meet them. We must dwell more on our strengths, assets, and potential as the really challenging frontier.

Conclusion

The current examples of violence and the factors encouraging it reflect our vacillation between the anachronistic culture of violence and the perplexing culture of constant change. We feel alienated and experience social disruption. Current demands for change are potentially dangerous because change activates a tendency to return to older, formerly effective, coping behaviors. Social disruption caused by change tends to increase violence as a means of coping at a time when violence is becoming a great danger to our survival.

America's current crises of violence make it difficult for us to cope with our changing world. Today's challenge, the crisis of violence, is really the crisis of man. This crisis is especially difficult because violence, a once useful but now increasingly maladaptive coping strategy, seems to be firmly rooted in human behavior patterns. We conquer the elements and yet end up facing our own image. Adaptation to a changing world rests on how effectively we can understand, channel, and redirect our aggressive energies. Then man can close his era of violence.

Summary

We are uniquely endowed both biologically and culturally to adapt to our environment. Although we are potentially capable of consciously determining the nature of our environment, our outmoded adaptive behavior—our violent aggression—keeps us from doing so.

Aggression is viewed as multidetermined. It is inherent, caused by frustration, or learned by imitation. Violent aggression is a form of attempted coping behavior that we in America as others elsewhere, use despite its potentially maladaptive and destructive results. Current examples of violence and the factors fostering it include assassination, the mass media, mental illness and homicide, firearms and resistances to restrictive gun legislation, and collective and sanctioned violence. These examples are considered from the perspectives of the changing nature of adaptation and the opportunities they offer for research. Among recommendations for resolving or reducing violence, the need for thoughtful research by behavioral scientists is stressed. But the major obstacle to removing violence from our society is our slowness to recognize that our anachronistic, violent style of coping with problems will destroy us in this technological era.

REFERENCES AND NOTES

1. L. Eiseley, *The Immense Journey* (Random House, New York, 1946).
2. D. N. Daniels, M. F. Gilula, F. M. Ochberg, Eds., *Violence and the Struggle for Existence* (Little, Brown, Boston, in press).
3. Dr. T. Bittker, C. Boelkins, Dr. P. Bourne, Dr. D. N. Daniels (co-chairman); Dr. J. C. Gillin, Dr. M. F. Gilula, Dr. G. D. Gulevich, Dr. B. Hamburg, Dr. J. Heiser, Dr. F. Ilfeld, Dr. M. Jackman, Dr. P. H. Leiderman, Dr. F. T. Melges, Dr. R. Metzner, Dr. F. M. Ochberg (co-chairman); Dr. J. Rosenthal, Dr. W. T. Roth, Dr. A. Siegel, Dr. G. F. Solomon, Dr. R. Stillman, Dr. R. Taylor, Dr. J. Tinklenberg, Dr. Edison Trickett, and Dr. A. Weisz.
4. *Webster's Third New International Dictionary* (Merriam, Springfield, Mass., 1966).
5. J. Gould and W. L. Kolb, *A Dictionary of the Social Sciences* (Free Press, New York, 1964); L. E. Hinsie and R. J. Campbell, *Psychiatric Dictionary* (Oxford Univ. Press, ed. 3, New York, 1960).
6. R. C. Boelkins and J. Heiser, "Biological aspects of aggression," in *Violence and the Struggle for Existence,* D. N. Daniels, M. F. Gilula, F. M. Ochberg, Eds. (Little, Brown, Boston, in press).
7. *The Natural History of Aggression,* J. D. Carthy and F. J. Ebling, Eds. (Academic Press, New York, 1964).
8. Th. Dobzhansky, *Mankind Evolving* (Yale Univ. Press, New Haven, 1962).
9. G. G. Simpson, "The study of evolution: Methods and present states of theory," in *Behavior and Evolution,* A. Roe and G. G. Simpson, Eds. (Yale Univ. Press, New Haven, 1958).
10. D. A. Hamburg, "Emotions in the perspective of human evolution," in *Expression of the Emotions in Man,* P. D. Knapp, Ed. (International Universities Press, New York, 1963).
11. C. Kluckhohn, "The limitations of adaptation and adjustment as concepts for understanding cultural behavior," in *Adaptation,* J. Romano, Ed. (Cornell Univ. Press, Ithaca, New York, 1949).
12. E. Silber, D. A. Hamburg, G. V. Coelho, E. B. Murphey, M. Rosenberg, L. I. Pearlin, *Arch Gen. Psychiat. 5,* 354 (1961).
13. D. A. Hamburg and J. E. Adams, *ibid.* 17, 277 (1967).

14. O. Fenichel, *The Psychoanalytic Theory of Neurosis* (Norton, New York, 1945).
15. K. Lorenz, *On Aggression* (Harcourt, Brace and World, New York, 1966).
16. A. Storr, *Human Aggression* (Atheneum, New York, 1968).
17. G. F. Solomon, "Case studies in violence," in *Violence and the Struggle for Existence,* D. N. Daniels, M. F. Gilula, F. M. Ochberg, Eds. (Little, Brown, Boston, in press).
18. J. P. Scott, *Aggression* (Univ. of Chicago Press, Chicago, 1958).
19. L. Berkowitz, *Aggression: A Social-Psychological Analysis* (McGraw-Hill, New York, 1962); J. Dollard, L. W. Doob, N. E. Miller, O. H. Mowrer, R. R. Sears, *Frustration and Aggression* (Yale Univ. Press, New Haven, 1939).
20. A. Bandura and R. H. Walters, *Social Learning and Personality Development* (Holt, Rinehart & Winston, New York, 1963); F. Ilfeld, "Environmental theories of aggression," in *Violence and the Struggle for Existence,* D. N. Daniels, M. F. Gilula, F. M. Ochberg, Eds. (Little, Brown, Boston, in press); M. E. Wolfgang and F. Ferracuti, *The Sub-Culture of Violence* (Barnes and Noble, New York, 1967).
21. R. Taylor and A. Weisz, "The phenomenon of assassination," in *Violence and the Struggle for Existence,* D. N. Daniels, M. F. Gilula, F. M. Ochberg, Eds. (Little, Brown, Boston, in press).
22. L. Z. Freedman, *Postgrad. Med.* 37, 650 (1965); D. W. Hastings, *J. Lancet* 85, 93 (1965); *ibid.,* p. 157; *ibid.,* p. 189; *ibid.,* p. 294.
23. "It's Russian roulette every day, said Bobby," San Francisco *Examiner* (6 June 1968).
24. J. Cottrel, *Anatomy of an Assassination* (Muller, London, 1966).
25. A. E. Siegel, "Mass media and violence," in *Violence and the Struggle for Existence,* D. N. Daniels, M. F. Gilula, F. M. Ochberg, Eds. (Little, Brown, Boston, in press; O. N. Larsen, Ed., *Violence and the Mass Media* (Harper and Row, New York, 1968).
26. E. A. Maccoby, "Effects of the mass media," in *Review of Child Development Research,* L. W. Hoffman and M. L. Hoffman, Eds. (Russell Sage Foundation, New York, 1964).
27. L. Berkowitz, *Psychol. Today* 2 (No. 4), 18 (1968).
28. H. T. Himmelweit, A. N. Oppenheim, P. Vince, *Television and the Child* (Oxford Univ. Press, New York, 1958)
29. W. Schramm, J. Lyle, E. B. Parker, *Television in the Lives of Our Children* (Stanford Univ. Press, Stanford, Calif., 1961).
30. A. Bandura, D. Ross, S. Ross, *J. Abnorm. Soc. Psychol.* 63, 575 (1961); *ibid.* 66, 3 (1963).
31. F. Wertham, *A Sign for Cain* (Macmillan, New York, 1966).
32. G. Mirams, *Quart. Film Radio Television* 6, 1 (1951).
33. Purdue Opinion Panel, *Four Years of New York Television* (National Association of Educational Broadcasters, Urbana, Ill., 1954).
34. Associated Press report of 25 July 1968; *Christian Science Monitor* article; New York *Times* (29 July 1968).
35. G. D. Gulevich and P. Bourne, "Mental illness and violence," in *Violence and the Struggle for Existence,* in D. N. Daniels, M. F. Gilula, F. M. Ochberg, Eds. (Little, Brown, Boston, in press.)
36. L. H. Cohen and H. Freeman, *Conn. State Med. J.* 9, 697 (1945).

37. H. Brill and B. Malzberg, *Mental Hospital Service (APA) Suppl. No. 153* (August 1962).

38. J. R. Rappaport and G. Lassen, *Amer. J. Psychiat.* 121, 776 (1964).

39. C. Babal *No Right to Bear Arms* (Paperback Library, New York, 1968).

40. C. A. deLeon, "Threatened homicide—A medical emergency," *J. Nat. Med. Assoc.* 53, 467 (1961).

41. J. C. Gillin and F. M. Ochberg, "Firearms control and violence," in *Violence and the Struggle for Existence,* D. N. Daniels, M. F. Gilula, F. M. Ochberg, Eds. (Little, Brown, Boston, in press).

42. D. N. Daniels, E. J. Trickett, J. R. Tinklenberg, J. M. Jackman, "The gun law controversy: Issues, arguments, and speculations concerning gun legislation," *Violence and the Struggle for Existence,* in D. N. Daniels, M. F. Gilula, F. M. Ochberg, Eds. (Little, Brown, Boston, in press).

43. Criminal Division, U.S. Department of Justice, *Firearms Facts* (16 June 1968); based in large part on the Federal Bureau of Investigation, *Uniform Crime Reports* (1967) (U.S. Government Printing Office, Washington, D.C., 1968).

44. F. Zimring, *"Is Gun Control Likely To Reduce Violent Killings?"* (Center for Studies in Criminal Justice, Univ. of Chicago Law School, Chicago, 1968).

45. *Congressional Quarterly,* "King's murder, riots spark demands for gun controls" (12 April 1968), pp. 805-815.

46. R. Harris, *The New Yorker* 44 (20 April 1968), p. 56.

47. E. Cleaver, *Ramparts* 7 (15 June 1968), p. 17.

48. *Amer. Rifleman* 116 (Nos. 2-5) (1968), various writings.

49. W. W. Herlihy, *ibid.,* 116 (No. 5), 21 (1968).

50. T. E. Bittker, "The choice of collective violence in intergroup conflict," in *Violence and the Struggle for Existence.* D. N. Daniels, M. F. Gilula, F. M. Ochberg, Eds. (Little, Brown, Boston, in press).

51. P. Lowinger, E. D. Luby, R. Mendelsohn, C. Darrow, *"Case study of the Detroit uprising: The troops and the leaders"* (Department of Psychiatry, Wayne State Univ. School of Medicine, and the Lafayette Clinic, Detroit, 1968); C. Darrow and P. Lowinger, "The Detroit uprising: A psychosocial study," in *Science and Psychoanalysis, Dissent,* J. H. Masserman, Ed. (Grune and Stratton, New York, 1968), vol. 13.

52. J. Spiegel, *Psychiat. Opinion* 5 (No. 3), 6 (1968).

53. J. D. Frank, *Sanity and Survival: Psychological Aspects of War and Peace* (Random House, New York, 1967); I. Ziferstein, *Amer. J. Orthopsychiat.* 37, 457 (1967).

54. D. Freeman, "Human aggression in anthropological perspective," in *The Natural History of Aggression,* J. D. Carthy and F. J. Ebling, Eds. (Academic Press, New York, 1964).

55. L. F. Richardson, *Statistics of Deadly Quarrels* (Boxwood Press, Pittsburgh, 1960).

56. F. Ilfeld and R. Metzner "Alternatives to violence; Strategies for coping with social conflict," in *Violence and the Struggle for Existence,* D. N. Daniels, M. F. Gilula, F. M. Ochberg, Eds. (Little, Brown, Boston, in press).

57. We thank Dr. D.A. Hamburg and DR. A. Siegel for their review and critique of this paper and M. Shapiro, C. DiMaria, and R. Franklin for their contributions in preparing this manuscript.

STUDY QUESTIONS

1. What two theses are presented by the authors?
2. How do the authors define *violence* and *aggression*?
3. How is adaptation distinguished from adjustment?
4. What do the authors mean when they state: "Every culture prescribes the range of coping behaviors available to its people . . . "? What is "coping behavior"? What are some forms of coping behavior permitted by our society; Prohibited by our society?
5. Compare and contrast coping behavior strategies. Sum up each of the three theories of aggression. What is the source of aggression according to each theory? What means of controlling or reducing violence is suggested by each theory? What theory do the authors prefer and why?
6. What is the author's explanation of the presidential assassinations.
7. What causal relations exist between violence on television and the consequent behavior of children?
8. What is the relation between mental illness and violence?
9. Which fact about guns is the most startling? Do you agree with the objections given here, to those opposing gun control legislation.
10. Explain "the legitimacy of violence is arbitrary . . ." Upon what does the psychology of sanctioned violence depend?
11. What are the four socio-psychological antecedents to ghetto uprisings?
12. What fundamental change of function has occurred regarding violent aggression?
13. What is the major obstacle to removing violence in our society?

3

WHAT VIOLENCE IS*

Newton Garver

Newton Garver teaches philosophy at the State University of New York, Buffalo. His articles appear in many journals. In the following selection, Garver examines the meaning of violence. He says, "The idea of violence in human affairs is much more closely connected with the idea of violation than it is with the idea of force." He classifies violence into four different kinds, based on two criteria: whether the violence is personal or institutionalized and whether the violence is overt or a kind of quiet (psychological) violence.

MOST PEOPLE deplore violence, many people embrace violence (perhaps reluctantly), and a few people renounce violence. But through all these postures there runs a certain obscurity, and it is never entirely clear just what violence is.

Those who deplore violence loudest and most publicly are usually identified with the status quo—school principals, businessmen, politicians, ministers. What they deplore is generally overt attacks on property or against the "good order of society." They rarely see violence in defense of the status quo in the same light as violence directed against it. At the time of the Watts riots in 1965 President Johnson urged Negroes to realize that nothing of any value can be won through violent means—an idea which may be true but which Johnson himself seemed to ignore in connection with the escalation of the Vietnam war he was simultaneously embarking upon. But the President [Johnson] is not the only one of us who deplores violence while at the same time perpetrating it, and a little more clarity about what exactly we deplore might help all around.

Those who renounce violence are equally hard to follow. Tolstoy, Gandhi, Muste stand out among the advocates of nonviolence of the past century and as one reads them it becomes clear that they do not all

---

*Reprinted by permission. A version of this article first appeared in *The Nation*.

45

renounce exactly the same thing. There is much that is concrete and detailed in the writings of these men, but nonetheless it is not easy to avoid the impression that "nonviolence" is really just morality itself rather than a specific commitment to eschew a certain well-defined sort of behavior.

Those who embrace violence are in a much better position, for they stand ready to embrace whatever is "inevitable" or "necessary" in the circumstances, and hence the question of just where violence begins or leaves off does not arise for them. But if we want to know about the nature and varieties of violence, it does not help to be told that violence is unavoidable or that it is a necessary means to some end. There is a question about understanding violence before we come to adopt a posture toward it, and it is to that question we now turn.

II

What I want to do is to present a kind of typology of violence. I want, that is, to try to make clear what some of the different types and kinds and forms of violence are, and thereby to give a perspective of the richness of this topic. Unfortunately, I can't begin saying what the types of violence are without saying first what it is I'm giving you a typology of. So let's begin with a definition of violence.

What is violence? That is a typical philosophical question. The psychiatrists and the sociologists are interested in the questions: why is there violence? what causes violence? That's not my concern—at least not my professional concern nor my concern here. What I'm interested in is the old-fashioned philosophical question: What is the nature or essence of violence? We can make a good start etymologically. The word 'violence' comes, of course, from the French, prior to that from the Latin, and you can find Greek roots if you're up to it—which I'm not. The Latin root of the word 'violence' is a combination of two Latin words—the word '*vis*' (force) and the past participle '*latus*' of the word '*fero*' (to carry). The latin word '*violare*' is itself a combination of these two words and its present participle '*violans*' is a plausible source for the word 'violence'—so that the word 'violence', in its etymological origin, has the sense of to carry force at or toward. An interesting feature of the etymology is that the word 'violation' comes from this very same source as the word 'violence', which suggests to us the interesting idea that violence is somehow a violation of something: that carrying force against something constitutes in one way or another a violation of it.

The idea of force being connected with violence is a very powerful one. There is no question at all that in many contexts the word 'force' is a synonym for the word 'violence'. This is particularly true if you talk about, for example, a violent blizzard: a violent blizzard is nothing but a blizzard with very great force. The same is true of a violent sea and other bits of violence in nature. It is simply some aspect of nature manifested to us with especially great force. But I don't want to talk about natural phenomena—certainly not meteorological phenomena. I want to talk instead about human phenomena. In human affairs violence cannot be equated with force.

One of the very first things to understand about violence in human affairs is that it is not the same thing as force. It is clear that force is often used on another person's body and there is no violence done. For example, if a man is drowning—thrashing around and is apparently unable to save himself—and you use the standard Red Cross life-saving techniques, you will use force against his body although certainly you won't be doing any violence to him. You will, in fact, be saving his life instead. To think so rigidly of force and violence being identical with one another that you call this sort of life-saving an act of violence is to have lost sight entirely of the significance of the concept. Similarly, surgeons and dentists use force on our bodies without doing violence to us.

The idea of violence in human affairs is much more closely connected with the idea of violation than it is with the idea of force. What is fundamental about violence in human affairs is that a person is violated. Now that is a tough notion to explain. It is easy enough to understand how you can violate a moral rule or a parking regulation, but what in the world does it mean to talk about "violating a person"? That, I think, is a very important question, and because it can give a fresh perspective on what it means to be human it deserves fuller consideration than I can give it in this context. If it makes sense to talk about violating a person, that just is because a person has certain rights which are undeniably, indissolubly, connected with his being a person. The very idea of natural rights is controversial since it is redolent of Scholasticism, but I find myself forced to accept natural rights in order to understand the moral dimension of violence. One of the most fundamental rights a person has is a right to his body—to determine what his body does and what is done to his body—because without his body he wouldn't be a person anymore. The most common way a person ceases to exist is that his body stops functioning—a point which appeals especially forcefully if you think of a person as a living, growing thing rather than as something static or as a substance in the traditional sense. Apart from a body what is essential to one's being a person is dignity in something like the existentialist sense. The dignity of a person does not consist in his remaining prim and proper or dignified and unruffled, but rather in his making his own decisions. In this respect what is fundamental about a person is radically different from what is fundamental, for example, about a dog. I have a dog. I don't expect him to make decisions: When I tell him to sit or to stay I expect him just to do it, not to decide. And, indeed, the way I have treated my dog, which seems to be a good way to treat a dog, is to train him to respond in a more or less mechanical way to certain commands. Now that, it seems to me, is to give a dog a very good place in life, at least as we have arranged it. However, to treat a human being that way is an affront to his dignity as a human being, just because it is essential to a human being that he have a kind of dignity or "autonomy," as Kant put it.

The right to one's body and the right to autonomy are undoubtedly the most fundamental natural rights of persons, but there are subsidiary ones that deserve mention as part of the background for our discussion of violence. One of these stems from the right to autonomy. It is characteristic of human action to be purposive and to have results and consequences, and freedom therefore is normally conceived as involving not only the right to decide what to do but also the right to dispose of or cope with the consequences of one's action. One aspect of this right is the right to the product of one's labor, which has played an important role in the theory of both capitalism and communism. Both Marx and Locke, in two entirely different traditions as we think of it nowadays, has a labor theory of economic value: that the inherent value of something is determined by the amount of labor that is required to produce it. It is one of the ironies of intellectual history that the right of persons to the product of their labor constitutes the basis for both Locke's defense of private property and Marx's attack on it. If we follow this line of thought to the extent that we consider one's property as an extension of his person, the scope of the concept of violence becomes greatly enlarged, perhaps in harmony with popular thought on the subject, at least on the part of propertied persons; but one should always bear in mind that a person can reconcile himself much more readily to loss of property than he can to loss of life.

If we say that the results of what a person does belongs to him, we should have in mind not only this kind of labor theory of value but also the more or less natural and expectable consequences of a person's action. One of Jean-Paul Sartre's most interesting plays, *Altona*, develops this theme. In this play Sartre depicts a young man who does things that would normally have very serious consequences, probably his death. At one time he defies the Nazis, at another time the American Military Government that is occupying the country. On both occasions his father intervenes and cuts him off from the normal, expected consequences of his actions, consequences which anybody else would have suffered. Sartre shows what an awful impact it has upon this man, as a person, to have the consequences of his actions cut off in this way. In the end this victim of paternalism is one of Sartre's rather hideous characters, sequestered in a room in the center of his father's grand mansion having hallucinations of crabs and visions of expiation.

Here then is an indication of what is involved in talking about the violation of a person, and it seems to me that violence in human affairs comes down to violating persons. With that in mind, let me turn now to discussion of the different types and forms of violence. Violence can be usefully classified into four different kinds based on two criteria, whether the violence is personal or institutionalized and whether the violence is overt or a kind of covert or quiet violence.

III

Overt physical assault of one person on the body of another is the most obvious form of violence. Mugging, rape, and murder are the flagrant "crimes of violence," and when people speak of the danger of violence in the streets it is usually visions of these flagrant cases that float before their minds. I share the general concern over the rising rate of these crimes, but at the same time I deplore the tendency to cast our image of violence just in the mold of these flagrant cases. These are cases where an attack on a human body is also clearly an attack on a person and clearly illegal. We must not tie these characteristics in too tight a package, for some acts of violence are intended as a defense of law or a benefit to the person whose body is beaten—e.g. ordinary police activity (not "police brutality")[1] and the corporal punishment of children by parents and teachers. The humbler cases are violence too, although the fact that policemen, teachers, and parents have socially defined roles which they invoke when they resort to violence indicates that these cases have institutional aspects that overshadow the purely personal ones. These institutional overtones make a great deal of difference but they cannot erase that there is violence done. Of course not all cases are so clear: I leave to the reader to ponder whether all sex acts are acts of violence, or just how to distinguish in practical terms those that are from those that are not. Whenever you do something to another person's body without his consent you are attacking not just a physical entity—you are attacking a person. You are doing something by force, so the violence in this case is something that is easily visible, has long been recognized as violence, and is a case of overt, personal violence.

In cases of war, what one group tries to do to another group is what happens to individuals in cases of mugging and murder. The soldiers involved in a war are responsible for acts of violence against "the enemy," at least in the sense that the violence would not have occurred if the soldiers had refused to act. (Of course some other violence might have occurred. But in any case I do not wish to try to assess blame or lesser evils.) The Nuremberg trials after World War II attempted to establish that individual soldiers are responsible morally and legally too, but this attempt overlooked the extent to which the institutionalization of violence changes its moral dimension. On the one hand an individual soldier is not acting on his own initiative and responsibility, and with the enormous difficulty in obtaining reliable information and making a timely confrontation of government claims, not even U.S. Senators, let alone soldiers and private citizens, are in a good position to make the necessary judgments about the justice of a military engagement. On the other hand a group does not have a soul and cannot act except through the agency of individual men. Thus there is a real difficulty in assigning responsibility for such institutional violence. The other side of the violence, its object, is equally ambiguous, for "the enemy" are being

---

[1] A persuasive account of the extent to which law itself can be a form of violence, rather than an alternative to it, is to be found in E. Z. Friedenberg's essay "A Violent Country" in the *New York Review*, October 20, 1966.

attacked as an organized political force rather than as individuals, and yet since a group does not have a body any more than it has a soul "the enemy" is attacked by attacking the bodies of individual men (and woman and children). Warfare, therefore, because it is an institutionalized form of violence, differs from murder in certain fundamental respects.

Riots are another form of institutionalized violence, although their warlike character was not widely recognized until the publication of the report of the President's National Advisory Commission on Civil Disorders (the "Riot" Commission). In a riot, as in a war, there are many instances of personal violence, and some persons maintain that the civil disorders are basically massive crime waves. But on the other hand there is also much of a warlike character. One of the characteristics of the Watts riot, as any will know who have read Robert Conot's very interesting book, *The Rivers of Blood, Years of Darkness,* is that in that riot the people who were supposed to be controlling the situation, the Los Angeles police and their various reinforcements, simply did not know basic facts about the community. In particular they did not know who was the person who could exercise a sort of leadership if the group were left alone and that person's hand was strengthened. One incident illustrates the sort of thing that happened. A Negro policeman was sent in plain clothes into the riot area and told to call back into the precinct whenever there was anything to report. He was told, furthermore, not to identify himself as a policeman under any conditions for fear of jeopardizing himself. At one point, he tried to intervene when some cops were picking on just altogether the wrong person and he ended up getting cursed and having his head bashed in by one of his fellow members of the Los Angeles police force. The police were in such a state that they couldn't even refrain from hitting a Negro policeman who was sent on a plain-clothes assignment into that area. In effect, the Los Angeles police and their various allies conducted what amounted to a kind of a war campaign. They acted like an army going out to occupy a foreign territory where they didn't know the people and didn't speak the language. The result was that their actions had the effect of breaking down whatever social structure there might have been. And the breakdown of the social structure then had the effect of releasing more and more overt violence. The military flavor of our urban disturbances has increased over the years, and 1967 saw the appearance not only of machine guns and automatic rifles but also of tanks and armored personnel carriers in Newark and Detroit, in what the Kerner Commission characterized as "indiscriminate and excessive use of force." For that reason the urban disorders that we've been having in recent summers are really a kind of institutionalized violence where there are two sides in combat with one another. It is quite different from a normal criminal situation where police act against individual miscreants.

Since these overt forms of violence are, on the whole, fairly easily recognized, let us go on to consider the other forms of violence, the quiet forms which do not necessarily involve any overt physical assault on anybody's person or property. There are both personal and institutional forms of quiet violence, and I would like to begin with a case of what we might call psychological violence, where individuals are involved as individuals and there are not social institutions responsible for the violation of persons that takes place. Consider the following news item:[2]

> PHOENIX, Ariz., Feb. 6 (AP)—Linda Marie Ault killed herself, policemen said today, rather than make her dog Beauty pay for her night with a married man.
> The police quoted her parents, Mr. and Mrs. Joseph Ault, as giving this account:
> Linda failed to return home from a dance in Tempe Friday night. On Saturday she admitted she had spent the night with an Air Force lieutenant.
> The Aults decided on a punishment that would "wake Linda up." They ordered her to shoot the dog she had owned about two years.
> On Sunday, the Aults and Linda took the dog into the desert near their home. They had the girl dig a shallow grave. Then Mrs. Ault grasped the dog between her hands, and Mr. Ault gave his daughter a .22-caliber pistol and told her to shoot the dog.
> Instead, the girl put the pistol to her right temple and shot herself.
> The police said there were no charges that could be filed against the parents except possibly cruelty to animals.

Obviously, the reason there can be no charges is that the parents did no physical damage to Linda. But I think your reaction might be the same as mine—that they really did terrible violence to the girl by the way they behaved in this situation. Of course one must agree that Linda did

---

[2] *New York Times*, February 7, 1968.

violence to herself, but that is not the whole account of the violence in this case. The parents did far more violence to the girl than the lieutenant, and the father recognized that when he said to a detective, "I killed her. I killed her. It's just like I killed her myself." If we fail to recognize that there is really a kind of psychological violence that can be perpetrated on people, a real violation of their autonomy, their dignity, their right to determine things for themselves, their right to be humans rather than dogs, then we fail to realize the full dimension of what it is to do violence to one another.

One of the most obvious transition cases between overt personal violence and quiet personal violence is the case of a threat. Suppose a robber comes into a bank with a pistol, threatens to shoot one of the tellers, and walks out with money or a hostage or both. This is a case of armed robbery, and we rightly lump it together with cases of mugging and assault, morally and legally speaking, even if everybody emerges from the situation without any bruises or wounds. The reason is that there is a clear threat to do overt physical violence. By means of such a threat a person very often accomplishes what he might otherwise accomplish by actual overt violence. In this case the robber not only gets as much loot but he also accomplishes pretty much the same thing with respect to degrading the persons he is dealing with. A person who is threatened with being shot and then does something which he certainly would never otherwise do is degraded by losing his own autonomy as a person. We recognize that in law and morals: If a person who is threatened with a revolver takes money out of a safe and hands it to the robber we don't say that the person who has taken the money out of the safe has stolen it. We say that that person acted under compulsion, and hence the responsibility for what is done does not lie with him but with the person who threatened him.

It is very clear, and very important, that in cases where there is a threat of overt physical violence that we acknowledge that a person acting under that sort of a threat loses his autonomy. Of course, he needn't surrender his autonomy: he could just refuse to hand over the loot. There can be a great deal of dignity in such a refusal, and one of the messages of Sartre's moral philosophy, his existentialism, is that whenever you act other than with full responsibility yourself for your own actions that you are acting in bad faith. Now that is a very demanding philosophy, but it is one which puts a great deal of emphasis upon autonomy and dignity in human action and is not to be lightly dismissed. Nevertheless we do not expect that people will act with such uncompromising strength and dignity. To recognize that people can be broken down by threats and other psychological pressures, as well as by physical attack, and that to have acted under threat or duress is as good an excuse before the law as physical restraint—these recognitions constitute acknowledgement of the pertinence of the concept of psychological violence.

Psychological violence often involves manipulating people. It often involves degrading people. It often involves a kind of terrorism one way or another. Perhaps these forms that involve manipulation, degradation and terror are best presented in George Orwell's book, *1984*. In that book the hero is deathly afraid of being bitten by a rat. He never is bitten by the rat, but he is threatened with the rat and the threat is such as to break down his character in an extraordinary way. Here what might be called the phenomenology of psychological violence is presented in as convincing a form as I know.

Apart from these cases of terror and manipulation and degradation there are certain other forms of psychological violence. One of the most insidious is what might be called the "Freudian rebuff."[3] The Freudian rebuff works something like this. A person makes a comment on the Vietnam war or on civil rights or on some other current topic. The person he is talking to then says, "Well, you're just saying that because of your Oedipal relations with your father." The original speaker naturally objects, "Don't be silly. Of course I had a father and all that. But look at the facts." And then he starts bringing out the journals and newspapers and presents facts and statistics from them. "You must have a terrible Oedipal complex; you're getting so excited about this." And the person then says, "Look, I've had some fights with my father, but I'm not hung-up on him, I just have normal spats and affection. I've read the paper and I have an independent interest in the civil rights question. It has nothing to do with my relations with my father." To which the response is, "Well, your denial just proves how deep your Oedipal complex is." This type of Freudian rebuff has the effect of

---

[3]Of course, this is an aspect of cocktail-party Freudianism rather than of psycho-analytic theory, and what Freud invented was not this little ploy but the concepts that were later distorted into it.

what John Henry Newman[4] called "poisoning the wells." It gives its victim just no ground to stand on. If he tried to stand on facts and statistics, they are discounted and his involvement is attributed to Freudian factors. If he tries to prove that he doesn't have the kind of psychological aberration in question, his very attempt to prove that he doesn't have it is taken to be evidence that he does. He can't get out of the predicament. It is like a quagmire in which the victim sinks deeper no matter which way he moves. So long as the proffered definition of the situation is imposed on him, a person has no way to turn: there is no possible sort of response that can extricate him from that charge laid upon him. To structure a situation against a person in such a manner does violence to him by depriving him of his dignity: no matter what he does there is no way at all, so long as he accepts the problem in the terms in which it is presented, for him to make a response that will allow him to emerge with honor.

Although this sort of cocktail-party Freudianism is not very serious in casual conversations, where the definition of the situation can be challenged or the whole matter just shrugged off, it must be kept in mind that there are many forms of this ploy and that sometimes the whole life and character of a person may be involved. A classic literary and religious version is the dispute between Charles Kingsley and John Henry Newman in the 19th century, in which Kingsley challenged Newman's integrity and ended up losing his stature as a Protestant spokesman, and which is written up in fascinating detail in Newman's *Apologia.* A political variation is the Marxian rebuff where, of course, it is because of your class standing that you have such and such a view, and if you deny that the class standing is influencing you in that way your very denial shows how imbued you are with the class ideology. Between parent and child as well as between husband and wife there are variations of this ploy which turn around the identification (by one insistent party) of love with some particular action or other, so that the other party must either surrender his autonomy or acknowledge his faithlessness.

The cases where this sort of psychological violence are damaging are those where the person structuring the situation is in some position of special authority. Another form particularly virulent in urban schools—

---

[4] In his famous debate with Charles Kingsley. See his *Apologia Pro Vita Sua*, conveniently available in a paperback edition, (Garden City: Doubleday, 1956).

and probably suburban schools too—is the teacher's rebuff. An imaginative child does something out of the ordinary, and the teacher's response is that he is a discipline problem. It now becomes impossible for the child to get out of being a problem. If he tries to do something creative he will be getting out of line and thereby "confirm" that he is a discipline problem. If he stays in line he will be a scholastic problem, thereby "confirming" that he did not have potential for anything but mischief. The result is a kind of stunted person typical of schools in large urban areas, where it is common for a child to enter the public schools half a year behind according to standard tests. Such a child has undoubtedly been a discipline problem during this time and the teacher has spent her effort trying to solve the discipline problem and keep him from getting out of line—that is, from learning anything.[5]

This last variation of the psychological rebuff brings us to the fourth general category of violence, institutionalized quiet violence. The schools are an institution, and teachers are hired not so much to act on their own in the classroom as to fulfill a predetermined role. Violence done by the teacher in the classroom may therefore not be personal but institutional, done while acting as a faithful agent of the educational system. The idea of such institutional violence is a very important one.

A clearer example of quiet institutional violence might be a well established system of slavery or colonial oppression, or the life of contemporary American ghettos. Once established such a system may require relatively little overt violence to maintain it. It is legendary that Southerners used to boast, "We understand our nigras. They are happy here and wouldn't want any other kind of life,"—and there is no reason to doubt that many a Southerner, raised in the system and sheltered from the recurrent lynchings, believed it quite sincerely. In that sort of situation it is possible for an institution to go along placidly, as we might say, with no overt disturbances and yet for that institution to be one that is terribly brutal and that does great harm to its victims and which, incidentally, at the same time brutalizes people who are on top, since they lose a certain measure of their human sensitivity.

---

[5] Among the many works commenting on this aspect of public education, I have found those of Edgar Friedenberg and Paul Goodman most instructive. See Paul Goodman, *Compulsory Miseducation*, New York, Horizon, 1964; Edgar Z. Friedenberg, *The Vanishing Adolescent*, Boston, Beacon Press, 1959, and *Coming of Age in America*, New York, Knopf, 1963.

There is more violence in the black ghettos than there is anywhere else in America—even when they are quiet. At the time of the Harlem riots in 1964 the Negro psychologist, Kenneth Clark, said that there was more ordinary, day-to-day violence in the life of the ghettos than there was in any day of those disturbances. I'm not sure exactly what he meant. The urban ghettos are places where there is a great deal of overt violence, much of it a kind of reaction to the frustrations of ghetto life. Fanon describes the similar phenomenon of the growth of violence within the oppressed community in the colonial situation in Algeria.[6] When people are suppressed by a colonial regime, when they lack the opportunities which they see other people, white people, around them enjoying, then they become frustrated and have great propensities to violence. The safest target for such angry, frustrated people are their own kind. The Algerians did their first violence to other Algerians, in part because it wasn't safe to do it to a Frenchman. And the same is largely true of the situation that has developed in our urban ghettos. It isn't safe for a person living in the ghettos, if he is feeling frustrated and at the point of explosion, to explode against somebody outside the ghetto; but he can do it to his kids, his wife, his brother and his neighbor, and society will tend to look the other way. So there is a good deal of overt violence in the black ghettos. Perhaps that is what Clark meant.

But we also have to recognize that there is sometimes a kind of quiet violence in the very operation of the system. Bernard Lafayette, who has worked in urban areas for both the American Friends Service Committee and the Southern Christian Leadership Conference, speaks angrily of the violence of the status quo: "The real issue is that part of the 'good order of society' is the routine oppression and racism committed against millions of Americans every day. That is where the real violence is."[7] The fact is that there is a black ghetto in most American cities which operates very like any system of slavery. Relatively little violence is needed to keep the institution going and yet the institution entails a real violation of the human beings involved, because they are systematically denied the options which are obviously open to the vast majority of the members of the society in which they live. A systematic denial of options is one way to deprive men of autonomy. If I

[6] Frantz Fanon, *The Wretched of the Earth*, New York, Grove Press, 1966.
[7] In *Soul Force*, February 15, 1968.

systematically deprive a person of the options that are normal in our society, then he is no longer in a position to decide for himself what to do. Any institution which systematically robs certain people of rightful options generally available to others does violence to those people.

Perhaps denying options would not do violence to people if each individual person was an island unto himself and individuality were the full truth about human life. But it is not. We are social beings. Our whole sense of what we are independent of the fact that we live in society and have open to us socially determined options. I am now writing. As I write I make many choices about what to say, some having to do with whole paragraphs, some with single words, and some with punctuation. These choices are dependent upon a social institution, language. Unless I knew the language, and unless there were a society of language speakers, I would have no options at all about what to say. The options opened to us by language are very important, but language is only one part of our society. There are many sorts of options which are open to us and important to us as individuals. It is how we act, how we choose with respect to socially defined options, that constitutes what we really are as human beings.

What we choose to do with respect to our socially defined options is much more important than which language or which system of property rights we inherit at birth—provided we have access to the options defined in the system. By suppressing options you deprive a person of the opportunity to be somebody because you deprive him of choices. The institutional form of quiet violence operates when people are deprived of choices in a systematic way by the very manner in which transactions normally take place, without any individual act being violent in itself or any individual decision being responsible for the system.

These, then, are the main types of violence that I see. By recognizing those types of violence we begin to get the whole question of violence into a much richer perspective than when we hear the Chief of Police deplore violence. Such a richer perspective is vitally necessary, because we cannot do anything about the violence in our society unless we can see it, and most of us do not see it very well. Conceptions and perceptions are closely dependent on one another, and perhaps having a better idea of what violence is will enable us to recognize more readily the many sorts of violence that surround our lives.

IV

In concluding I would like to call attention to two aspects of violence. The first is that the concept of violence is a moral concept, but not one of absolute condemnation. Very often psychologists and sociologists and other scientists and students of animal behavior avoid the word "violence" just because it does have a moral connotation. The word "aggression" is sometimes used instead in some of the literature in psychology, and it is prominent in the title of Konrad Lorenz's recent book on animal behavior and aggression.[8] They choose this word "aggression" because it lacks the moral connotations of the term "violence." I think it is important to recognize that the concept of violence is a moral concept, and that the moral elements come in through the fact that an act of violence is a violation of a person. I think that it is also important to recognize that the normal pattern of moral discourse allows for excuses and rationalization. We don't expect people never to do anything which is at all wrong: we allow for excuses.[9] Sartre's very hard line, that excuses undermine the dignity and moral strength of the person being excused, has not really won the day in law courts or in the general moral view; or perhaps what Sartre meant is that we should never allow ourselves excuses rather than that we should never allow them to others. When a person commits an act of violence he is not necessarily to be condemned, though he does have some explaining to do. The fact that we would require an excuse from him, or some justification of his behavior, indicates that a person's doing an act of violence puts the burden of proof on him; but it doesn't suffice to show that the case has gone against him yet.

The second thing I want to say is that it is entirely clear to me that there are degrees of violence. All these various forms of violence are indeed violence, but if I simply say of an act or an institution that it is violent I have not yet said enough to give a clear evaluation of that act. I must also take account of how *much* violence it does to persons affected. Unfortunately this is easier said than done. It might at first be

---

[8] A classic study in psychology is John Dollard *et al, Frustration and Aggression,* New Haven, Yale, 1939. See also A. Buss, *The Psychology of Aggression,* New York, Wiley, 1961; K. Lorenz, *On Aggression,* New York, Harcourt Brace, 1966.

[9] The late Prof. John L. Austin called the attention of moral philosophers to the importance of excuses in moral discourse. See "A Plea for Excuses", *Philosophical Papers,* London, Oxford University Press, 1961.

thought that overt violence is always worse than quiet violence, but that rule does not hold generally except in the case of murder; in fact physical injury often heals more readily than psychological damage. It is more plausible to argue that institutional violence is always of greater harm than personal violence, but that obviously depends on the degree of violence on each side—which means that we must be able to judge the degree of violence in an act or an institution independent of the kind of violence involved. What we need is a scale for measuring degrees of violence, and we don't have one. Still there are degrees of violence, and it is possible to achieve considerable inter-subjective agreement about comparisons of pairs of cases.

STUDY QUESTIONS

1. How does Garver define "violence" in the etymological sense? Does this definition follow his own interpretation of violence?
2. How does he relate the term *force* to "violence in human affairs"? How does he relate the term *violation* to "violence in human affairs"?
3. What does Garver say are two of the "most fundamental rights" a person has? Which do you consider to be the most important? Explain. What are some of the "subsidiary rights" and how are they related to the "fundamental rights"?
4. What is the "irony" involved in the conception of private property by Marx and Locke?
5. What are the consequences of cutting off "natural or expectable consequences of a person's actions" according to Sartre?
6. What are the two criteria for classifying violence? What are the four types of violence, according to Garver?
7. In what ways does warfare, as an institutionalized form of violence, differ from murder, which is a personal form of violence?
8. According to Garver, how do riots differ from warfare? Comment upon and criticize his argument with regard to the incident during the Watts riot.

9. Does he consider any forms of violence to be "easily distinguishable or obvious"? If so, which ones?

10. What is "psychological violence"? What does it often "involve"? What do you think of the incident involving Linda Marie Ault? Do you agree with the conclusion reached by the police? Why or why not? What does Garver say?

11. Is "threat of overt physical violence" also violence?

12. What is wrong with using the term *aggression* to replace the term *violence*, according to Garver?

13. Which type of violence do you consider to be most harmful? Least harmful? Explain. What do you think Garver would say?

4

THE JUSTIFICATION OF VIOLENCE*

Robert Audi

Robert Audi (1941-   ) teaches philosophy at the University of Texas. He was a Woodrow Wilson Fellow, and he has received a prize for an article on violence from the Council for Philosophical Studies. Audi defines violence as either physical or psychological attack of a particular type. He then exhibits the complexities involved in arguing against any use of violence, as well as those arguments attempting to justify the use of violence itself.

VIOLENCE IS the physical attack upon, or the vigorous physical abuse of, or vigorous physical struggle against, a person or animal; or the highly vigorous psychological abuse of, or the sharp, caustic psychological attack upon, a person or animal; or the highly vigorous, or incendiary, or malicious and vigorous, destruction or damaging of property or potential property.

PRELIMINARY THEORETICAL CONSIDERATIONS
CONCERNING THE JUSTIFICATION OF VIOLENCE

In discussing the justification of violence I shall be primarily concerned with the sorts of considerations relevant to deciding whether its use is morally justified. After outlining what some of these considerations are, I shall go on in the next section to show some of their implications for various important views, most of them well known, about the conditions under which violence is morally justified.

The moral position I shall propose will be quite general. This should not be surprising: if I have been correct about how many ways there are in which people can do violence, then we should not ask about the justification of violence in the abstract; we must consider what kind of violence is in question, and this forces us to examine a very wide range

---

*"The Meaning and Justification of Violence" by Robert Audi, from *Violence,* edited by Jerome A. Shaffer. Copyright ©1971 by David McKay Company, Inc. Reprinted by permission of David McKay Company, Inc.

of actions and activities. I shall be primarily concerned, however, with violence contemplated as a strategy for achieving social reform, particularly where the reform envisaged is regarded as the rectification of grave moral wrongs, and even where revolution is considered necessary to achieve this reform. At the present time, violence of this sort is perhaps more controversial than any other sort, though the question of the conditions, if any, under which one nation is justified in making war on another is also important and difficult. The position I shall take on the justification of violence will, I hope, provide a way of dealing with this latter question; but I shall not have space to address it explicitly. The question of the justification of violence in purely personal affairs is also an important one; but I shall only outline how my position would lead us to deal with the question.

In discussing the justification of violence as a strategy for achieving social reform, we must first recognize considerations of justice: as virtually everyone would grant, to say that a strategy, policy, or course of action would be unjust is to produce a moral consideration against it, one which is normally—and perhaps always—morally conclusive. It is equally clear that to say that something would be just is to produce a moral consideration in favor of it . . . .   In addition to considerations of justice we must also recognize, in discussing the justification of violence as a strategy for achieving social reform considerations of freedom: whether the use of violence would enhance or diminish human freedom . . . .

The third consideration relevant to the justification of violence as a strategy for achieving social reform, is what we may roughly call

welfare: that some action or program of action increases human happiness, and especially that it reduces human suffering, is a consideration which is nearly always relevant to any moral assessment of it . . . . It is worth making at least a very rough distinction between personal and social violence: personal violence has nonpolitical motives and is perpetrated by a single person or small group of persons against another person or small group; social violence is violence by a group of people, almost always directed against the state or against another group of people, and usually perpetrated for political reasons. A person's shooting an acquaintance would usually be a paradigm of personal violence; a large riot resulting in extensive personal injury would be a paradigm of social violence. It seems somewhat unnatural to speak of violence done by one army to another as social violence, and it is probably better to call this simply military violence, though it is certainly social as opposed to personal. We also need to distinguish between violence to persons and violence to property or other inanimate things; and it is important to distinguish homicidal from nonhomicidal violence; and morally injurious violence—violence which violates someone's rights—from morally excusable violence, that is, violence which does not violate anyone's rights, as in the case of most violent athletic contests. Perhaps we should also distinguish hand-to-hand violence, as in the case of a fist fight, from violence "at a distance"—such as sniping, shelling, and bombing. There also seems to be an important difference between defensive and offensive violence, the former being violence undertaken on a reasonable belief that using it is necessary to protect one's moral rights, the latter being violence undertaken in order to subjugate someone or otherwise violate his moral rights. But this is a very difficult distinction to draw, nor do defensive and offensive violence seem to exhaust the possibilities of violence, since spontaneous violence might well be of neither kind.

What seems of greatest philosophical interest at present among the kinds of violence just mentioned is social violence, both to people and to property, homicidal and nonhomicidal, defensive and offensive, and whether hand-to-hand or done at a distance. In particular, I am concerned with the justifiability of such forms of violence in civil disobedience, in resistance, in revolution, and in attempts to achieve social progress that cannot be placed in any of these three categories. In discussing each case I shall appeal primarily to the three moral principles outlined above, and I shall proceed from arguing the inadequacy of various mistaken views about the justifiability of violence to some constructive suggestions about its use in civil disobedience, resistance, revolution, and social reform. Although the discussion will be focused on violence, what I have to say will have important application to questions concerning the justification of force as a strategy for achieving social reform and to various other moral questions concerning policies of social action.

This is not meant to suggest that the principles proposed have no application to the justification of personal violence; as moral principles of the most general sort, at least one of them should have an indirect bearing on any moral issue. But in a great many cases, particularly in deciding what moral obligations one individual has to another individual of his acquaintance, their bearing is very often only indirect: they may be appealed to in justifying the subsidiary moral principles which "govern" much of our conduct toward other individuals; but a great many of our typical obligations toward other individuals, for example, to do what we have promised to do, have their immediate basis in these more specific principles. To apply this to a case of personal violence, imagine a man who is contemplating beating his wife. My position does not imply that in deciding whether it would be right to do this he is free to appeal directly to the three general principles; as the wording of the principles suggests, they are intended to apply primarily to policies, strategies, practices, and other general prescriptions of conduct. Their rigorous application to the kind of case imagined would, I think, support the principle that (possibly with a few very special exceptions) we ought not to beat people. I would also hold, though I cannot argue for it here, that my principles would support both some form of the ordinary moral principles requiring truth-telling and promise-keeping, and the ordinary moral conviction that people in certain special relations to others, such as parents and children, acquire special obligations. None of this implies that it is never morally right to call ordinary moral principles into question: the point is simply that in deciding what is morally obligatory or permissible in our relations with other individuals, we cannot bypass moral principles ordinarily relevant to the kind of situation in question, though where two such principles conflict, we may in most cases appeal to one or more of the three general principles.

Let us take first the extreme view that no one is ever justified in using violence. The natural thing to say here is that if violence is necessary to stop a Hitler from carrying out his planned atrocities, then it should be used. Most people would find it hard to deny this, but advocates of nonviolence might well argue that in fact it is never necessary to use violence, even to stop a man like Hitler, particularly if nonviolent protests are used at the first signs of evil. Although I find this claim highly implausible, neither a philosopher nor anyone else can assess it, as applied to an actual case, without a thorough analysis of the facts regarding various societies. But what chiefly needs to be said here is that it is certainly conceivable that a man like Hitler might be stopped only through violence; and insofar as there is good reason to think that only violence can stop him, the use of at least some violence, especially nonhomicidal violence aimed at bringing about a coup or forcing the needed change in social policy, might obviously be justified by the moral principles to which I am appealing.

Another extreme position would be that violence is always justified if it is the most efficient means of throwing off oppression or rectifying some other form of justice. This position seems almost as implausible as the first: clearly injustice and suffering created by the violence might substantially outweigh the burden of using a less efficient means of reform. Suppose that nonviolent protest could bring down an oppressive but unstable regime in a somewhat longer time than would be required by the use of violence. If it were evident that the violence would probably involve suffering and deaths, the nonviolent protest would almost certainly be preferable. Here it is important to mention something which seems both obvious and important, but which is much too rarely taken into account in discussions of violence and revolution: that there is simply no way to compare with any precision the moral "cost" of taking a man's life, especially an innocent man's life, with the moral value of reducing suffering or eliminating oppression or some other form of injustice. No doubt there is a level of atrocity at which almost anyone would say—and could justifiably say—that there is so much oppression, injustice, or suffering that if, in order to improve the situation substantially, we have to do something that might well take an innocent man's life we ought still to do it. To be sure, if it is a certainty that some innocent person must die, particularly if his identity is known, the situation becomes even more problematic and violence would be much more difficult—perhaps impossible—to justify. It seems clear that in deciding whether to use violence that might result in death, especially the death of someone not guilty of whatever wrong must justify the use of violence in the first place, we have to make every possible effort to find a nondeadly alternative; and we should be extremely careful not to exaggerate the moral outrage that requires rectification, particularly if we regard ourselves as the victims. But there is no simple way, perhaps no way at all, to answer the question how to weigh the taking of lives, especially of people innocent or largely innocent of the moral wrongs we want to rectify, against the moral gains we might make through their rectification. The principles of justice, maximization of freedom, and maximization of welfare suggest why this should be so: for how can we say how much injustice we do to a man in taking his life, or how much freedom or happiness we deprive him of? Given that the preservation of human life is of very great moral value on almost any moral outlook, and certainly on the principles proposed above, this is surely one of the most powerful arguments that can be brought against most of the typical uses of violence.

Two other views that deserve mention are (a) that violence of the sort we are concerned with—social violence done out of a genuinely moral desire to achieve social change—cannot be justified unless all channels of nonviolent protest have been exhausted, and (b) that violence is never justified in a democratic society. Regarding (a), it is not clear that there usually *is* any definite number of channels of nonviolent protest, or what it takes to exhaust a channel of protest. Yet even assuming that there were a definite number and that we could exhaust them, this might take so long and allow so much moral wrong in the meantime that some degree of nonhomicidal violence, and especially violence to property, would be warranted if it could be reasonably argued to be necessary to rectifying the moral wrongs in question. If nonviolent means of eliminating oppressive curfews and arbitrary travel restrictions, or of providing a minority group with the rights of citizens, would take many years, whereas damaging a few nonresidential buildings could achieve the needed changes in a few months or a year, the latter course could perhaps be justified by the principles of justice, maximization of freedom, and maximization of welfare. This point depends, of course, not only on the view that violence is not "by definition" unjustifiable, but also on the view that certain kinds of damage to property constitute violence; yet I believe I have argued adequately for these views in defending my analysis of the concept of violence. I would not claim, however, that a situation of the sort envisaged here is probable; more important, I am certainly not denying that there is a strong prima facie obligation to try a reasonable amount of nonviolent protest before using violence, nor would I claim that we can usually be at all sure that social violence can be prevented from becoming homicidal. But even the minimal claims I have made suggest that we cannot reasonably hold that violence is never justified unless all channels of nonviolent protest have been exhausted.

Regarding (b), the thesis that social violence of the sort that

concerns us is never justified in a democratic society, I would first want
to say that much depends on what we mean by 'democratic.' If it
means something like 'such that political power lies in the hands of the
people,' than the thesis is surely false. For the majority of people in a
society could be, and indeed at times have been, deceived into accepting or voting for measures whose injustice might in some cases be
eradicable only by violent, though not necessarily homicidal, protest.
If, on the other hand, 'democratic' is used, as it often is nowadays, in
such a way that a society is not considered democratic unless certain
moral rights are guaranteed and the government has a certain minimum
concern for the welfare of the citizens, then there is no clear answer to
the question whether violence is ever justified in a democratic society.
For it is not clear that the term 'democratic,' used this way, would ever
apply to a society in which the three principles I am appealing to are
seriously violated. In any case, the general position I want now to
propose should enable us to deal with the issues concerning the justification of violence regardless of the kind of political system with respect
to which they arise.

What I propose is that in deciding whether violence would be
justified in a given case in which it is being considered as a means of
correcting certain grave moral wrongs, we should ascertain its probable
consequences for justice, freedom, and human welfare, and compare
these with the probable consequences of the most promising nonviolent
alternative(s) we can think of on careful reflection, choosing the course
of action which satisfies, or comes closest to satisfying, the require-
ments of the principles of justice, maximization of freedom, and
maximization of welfare. The restriction to cases in which violence is
being considered as a means of correcting certain grave moral wrongs is
important: these would have to be cases in which a serious attempt has
been made, or at least considered, to solve the problem through legal or
other nonviolent procedures; and they would usually be cases of serious
injustice, such as deprivations of freedom, though certain other serious
moral wrongs—such as a government's neglecting the welfare of its
people—might sometimes justify the consideration of some forms of
violence. It would certainly not do to say that, regardless of the moral
grievance and regardless of whether nonviolent means have been tried,
it is morally legitimate to consider using violence; and while I believe
this sort of restriction would follow from the principles I am using, it

seems best to include it at the outset in the interest of explicitness and brevity.

It is important to reemphasize my position that considerations of justice and freedom have priority over considerations of welfare. In comparing violent and nonviolent strategies of reform, our first concern should be to determine what would establish, or come closest to establishing, justice and the maximum freedom possible within the limits of justice. Secondarily, we should consider the consequences for welfare of adopting a violent as opposed to a nonviolent strategy; but these considerations could be decisive only where the more fundamental considerations weighed equally in favor of some violent and some nonviolent strategy, or perhaps, with the qualifications suggested earlier, where a huge gain in welfare is balanced against a minor injustice. Suppose that a group of young men who have vigorously protested the Vietnam War have very good evidence that records of their public protests are being kept by their draft boards and will be used unfairly against them, say in drafting them as a punitive measure. They might face the alternatives of violently breaking into the office and burning all its records or, on the other hand, taking the case to the courts. My point here would be that the most important consideration should be what is required by the principles of justice and freedom; and as I see it they would here require, assuming there is legal recourse for the grievance, that efforts be made to take the case to the courts: for the men to violate laws which the great majority of others respect and obey, often with considerable sacrifice, would be a prima facie violation of the requirement that benefits and burdens be distributed equally, and hence a prima facie injustice; and breaking into the office would be, prima facie, an unjustified violation of others' rights and an interference with their freedom to carry out their regular jobs. Even if it could be shown that all concerned would be happier if the men simply broke into the office and burned the records, this would not be a substantial consideration in favor of the violent alternative, and it is worth pointing out that the publicity which injustice receives from court proceedings is often an important step toward reform, even if the case is initially lost and sometimes when it is lost in the highest courts.

Let us now complicate the example by supposing that the men go to the very highest court and lose. What now should they do? Much depends on whether they lost the principle that punitive use of the draft is unjust or simply failed to win the point that their draft board was planning it. Suppose they lose the latter point. What then? For one thing, this may indicate some weakness in their evidence against their draft board: secondly, in many societies, nonviolent resistance would in this case be both the morally courageous course of action and most likely to arouse the conscience of people who might help. If, on the other hand, we suppose that the men's evidence against their draft board is of the sort a reasonable man would consider conclusive, but that they lost because their witnesses were afraid to testify, then the case becomes even more problematic. One consideration not yet mentioned would be the kind and degree of immorality of the war for which they were to be drafted: another would be what they might be able to do by some new nonviolent attempt to expose those who have perpetrated the injustice against them and their witnesses. There are other considerations, and I cannot now go into sufficient detail to try to settle the question, though perhaps enough has been said to suggest that the kind of limited violence envisaged here is not obviously impossible to justify under any circumstances whatever, even if it does appear that in a country like America today nonviolent protest would be morally preferable. The case would have been equally complicated had we supposed that, in the highest court of the land, the men had lost the principle that punitive use of the draft, especially against political dissenters, is unjust. Here we would have an even larger issue which might well warrant the consideration, though not necessarily the adoption, of revolution.

There are, of course, a number of difficulties confronting the view I propose regarding the justification of violence. I have already mentioned the impossibility of weighing with any precision the moral cost of taking a human life, especially an innocent life, against moral gains in justice, freedom, and welfare. But this is likely to be a serious problem for any plausible position on the justification of violence, and we can at least say that there is one kind of case in which some weighing might be possible: when the risks to human life of undertaking violence can be compared with the risks to it of abstaining from violence. Thus, if violence that would probably cost about a hundred lives could be shown necessary to save thousands, it would presumably be justified if it did not have certain other morally undesirable consequences such as the brutalization of a large number of people.

Secondly, there are profound difficulties in measuring justice or injustice, freedom or its curtailment, and happiness or suffering. It would be wrong to conclude, however, that there are not even rough standards which are in practice very useful. While the notions of equality and of a justified exception to the principle that men should be treated equally are vague, it is nonetheless clear that denying various civil liberties on grounds of color is not a justified inequality, whereas denying voting privileges to children is; and a great many injustices, particularly those serious enough to warrant the consideration of violence, are equally obvious. Moreover, even if we grant that there is an area of reasonable disagreement concerning a large number of freedoms, there is wide agreement on such fundamental freedoms as freedom of speech, freedom of worship, and freedom of personal movement; and these are the sorts of freedoms whose curtailment would be appealed to in most cases in which considerations of freedom might warrant the use of violence.

Finally, it is clear that there are rough indices of suffering and happiness which make possible at least judgments about the suffering or happiness of one person or group as compared to that of another or to their own suffering of happiness at different times: we can consider disease as opposed to physical well-being; psychological well-being (insofar as this can be measured without indulging any moral prejudice); poverty as opposed to comfortable income; observations and subjective reports of pain, tension, and malaise, as opposed to observations and subjective reports of zest, comfort, and satisfaction; and proportion of things done or submitted to that are wanted as opposed to unwanted.

Let me now comment briefly on the implications of my position for the use of violence in civil disobedience, resistance, revolution, and social reform. To begin with civil disobedience, one may reasonably question whether there is any kind of violence with which it is logically compatible. Certainly in the clear cases of civil disobedience the protest is both nonviolent and orderly; and if we think of civil disobedience as undertaken in protest against some particular law(s), but out of respect for law as an institution, one may well question whether violence could be a part of it. Suppose, however, that a group of students decided to block the pathway of some unarmed fellow students engaging in military drill and soon to go to war; and suppose the protesters were unarmed and planned not to use violence. If violence broke out but remained on the level of mild fisticuffs, with the protesters fighting only defensively, and if the protesters were willing to accept punishment if the courts demanded it, would we have to say that they had not succeeded in practicing civil disobedience? The answer to this question does not seem to be simply that they did not succeed, though it perhaps would be if, even without having planned to use violence, the protesters did initiate it. Civil disobedience requires that those practicing it be making a reasoned attempt to appeal to the conscience of others; they must not be attempting to impose their will on others through the use of force, which they would certainly be doing if violence were a calculated part of civil disobedience. On the other hand, if violence "spontaneously" breaks out, particularly where the protesters fight only defensively, it is entirely possible that we could speak of their having succeeded in committing civil disobedience. Perhaps we could say that in certain cases civil disobedience may be accompanied by violence, even on the part of those committing the disobedience, but the violence must not have been calculated; nor can a protest count as civil disobedience if the protesters respond to violence with substantially greater violence than is required for self-defense. If violence has any place in civil disobedience, then, it seems to be a very minor and restricted one.

The case with resistance is different, and what chiefly needs to be said here is that there is no moral justification for the use of large-scale social violence except where injustice or some other form of moral wrong is very serious and where nonviolent means of rectification have been carefully considered and, if possible, attempted. It seems reasonable to maintain that justice, maximization of freedom, and maximization of welfare should be the guiding principles; and they should be applied in the light of questions like the following: What are the chances of death and in how many cases? How many are likely to suffer violence, and what sort of violence would it be—bodily violence or violence to property? To what extent are those who use violence likely to be brutalized by it or to come to use it indiscriminately, either at the time in question or at a later time? How much violence is likely to be evoked as a *response* to the violence being considered? Of those who may suffer violence, how many are guilty of creating or perpetuating the moral wrongs which might justify the violence, and how many are innocent or largely innocent in this respect? How effective will the contemplated violence be in rectifying the wrongs it is meant to reduce or remove? Is the immorality which might warrant violence getting worse or better, and what is the likelihood of dealing with it non-violently in a reasonable length of time? Is violence to be definitely planned, or is it simply to be approved should certain circumstances arise?

Questions like these seem to be equally relevant to the justifiability of attempting a revolution. But since revolution almost necessarily requires very extensive violence, even greater care must be taken in attempting to justify it. The questions I suggest we ask in considering whether to use violence are very difficult; and it is not surprising that many of them have not been faced, much less answered, by advocates of violence. Yet it is only through rigorously pursuing these and similar questions that we can weigh the consequences for justice, freedom, and welfare, of using a violent as opposed to a nonviolent method of moral rectification, and decide whether the best course of action would be nonviolent protest within the law, civil disobedience, resistance, or revolution, which is likely to require widespread and deadly violence.

Regarding the use of violence to achieve social reforms that do not qualify as the correction of injustice—such as certain improvements in state services or in the material well-being of large groups of people—it seems reasonable to say that particularly where material well-being is already at a level representing a secure and not uncomfortable life, any appreciable violence to persons could not be justified. For even assuming that there is no legal or other nonviolent way of achieving the goal, violence would probably require injustice to someone, and I am supposing that the gains in happiness that might result would not outweigh the injustice done. Suppose that a highway, which was a mere convenience to a large number of people, would have to go through a place where some American Indians who had been living there for generations were determined to stay unless bodily ejected. If we assume that neither they nor the larger community has a clear right in the dispute, probably the state would not be justified in using violence (or even force) to remove them, even if the convenience to the community could be reasonably claimed to outweigh substantially the inconvenience to them. Of course, if the disparity between what the community stands to gain and what a few stand to lose in being forced, violently if necessary, to comply with the community's wishes, becomes very great, the issue becomes more complex and we may begin to ask how much convenience a small group has a *right* to deny to a much larger group, especially to the community as a whole. In this case the minority's insistence on what it wants could be unjust, since it could be an interference with the community's freedom to do what it has a right to do; but it still seems clear that, with perhaps very few exceptions, if gains in happiness which do not represent what anyone has a right to should require violence to persons, the violence should not be used. For surely it is reasonable to give considerations of justice very high priority over considerations of welfare, as I have already suggested in discussing possible conflicts among the three moral principles proposed; and doing violence to someone, at least violence of the sort relevant here, unless it can be shown to be required to rectify some serious injustice, is certainly doing him an injustice.

STUDY QUESTIONS

1. Do you agree with Audi's definition of violence? Can violence be purely psychological?
2. What are the three main factors to consider regarding the justification of violence?
3. On what grounds might one argue that violence is never justified?
4. On what grounds can one argue that violence is justified?
5. Is it true that violence is not justified in society because one can "use channels"? Or is it true that violence is never justified in a democratic society? Defend one of these arguments.

5

NON-VIOLENCE IS THE WAY*

Martin Luther King, Jr.

Martin Luther King, Jr. was a Baptist Minister and President of the Southern Leadership Conference, and the acknowledged leader of the civil rights movement in America until his assassination in 1968. An eloquent speaker, Dr. King united blacks and whites by the force of his love and by his dedication to the people. He was honored in his lifetime, receiving the Nobel Prize for Peace in 1964, and in his death he became a symbol of black martyrdom. In the months preceding his assassination, Dr. King had moved to a more militant position in regard to racial issues and a position highly critical of United States foreign policy. In the following article, King replies to a group of Birmingham clergymen who objected to his tactics. He argues that the only path to negotiations is to create a crisis by non-violent means so that the community which has refused to negotiate must negotiate. He believes in obeying the law but only just law, which he defines as one which upholds human dignity. If repression is not relieved by non-violent ways then violence will result.

April 12, 1963

WE THE UNDERSIGNED clergymen are among those who, in January, issued "An Appeal for Law and Order and Common Sense," in dealing with racial problems in Alabama. We expressed understanding that honest convictions in racial matters could properly be pursued in the courts, but urged that decisions of those courts should in the meantime be peacefully obeyed.

Since that time there had been some evidence of increased forbearance and a willingness to face facts. Responsible citizens have undertaken to work on various problems which cause racial friction and unrest. In Birmingham, recent public events have given indication that we all have opportunity for a new constructive and realistic approach to racial problems.

However, we are now confronted by a series of demonstrations by some of our Negro citizens, directed and led in part by outsiders. We recognize the natural impatience of people who feel that their hopes are slow in being realized. But we are convinced that these demonstrations are unwise and untimely.

We agree rather with certain local Negro leadership which has called for honest and open negotiation of racial issues in our area. And we believe this kind of facing of issues can best be accomplished by citizens of our own metropolitan area, white and Negro, meeting with their knowledge and experience of the local situation. All of us need to face that responsibility and find proper channels for its accomplishment.

Just as we formerly pointed out that "hatred and violence have no sanction in our religious and political traditions," we also point out that such actions as incite to hatred and violence, however technically peaceful those actions may be, have not contributed to the resolution of our local problems. We do not believe that these days of new hope are days when extreme measures are justified in Birmingham.

We commend the community as a whole, and the local news media and law enforcement officials in particular, on the calm manner in which these demonstrations have been handled. We urge the public to continue to show restraint should the demonstrations continue, and the law enforcement officials to remain calm and continue to protect our city from violence.

We further strongly urge our own Negro community to withdraw support from these demonstrations, and to unite locally in working peacefully for a better Birmingham. When rights are consistently denied, a cause should be pressed in the courts and in negotiations among local leaders, and not in the streets. We appeal to both our white and Negro citizenry to observe the principles of law and order and common sense.

C. C. J. CARPENTER, D.D., LL.D., Bishop of Alabama; JOSEPH A. DURICK, D.D., Auxiliary Bishop, Diocese of Mobile-Birmingham; RABBI MILTON L. GRAFMAN, Temple Emanu-El, Birmingham, Alabama; BISHOP PAUL HARDIN, Bishop of the Alabama-West Florida Conference of the Methodist Church; BISHOP NOLAN B. HARMON, Bishop of the North Alabama Conference of the Methodist Church; GEORGE M. MURRAY, D.D., LL.D., Bishop Coadjutor, Episcopal Diocese of Alabama; EDWARD V. RAMAGE, Moderator, Synod of the Alabama Presbyterian Church of the United States; EARL STALLINGS, Pastor, First Baptist Church, Birmingham, Alabama.

April 16, 1963

MY DEAR FELLOW CLERGYMEN:

While confined here in the Birmingham city jail, I came across your recent statement calling my present activities "unwise and untimely." Seldom do I pause to answer criticism of my work and ideas. If I sought to answer all the criticisms that cross my desk, my secretaries would have little time for anything other than such correspondence in the course of the day, and I would have no time for constructive work. But since I feel that you are men of genuine good will and that your criticisms are sincerely set forth, I want to try to answer your statement in what I hope will be patient and reasonable terms.

I think I should indicate why I am here in Birmingham, since you have been influenced by the view which argues against "outsiders coming in." I have the honor of serving as president of the Southern Christian Leadership Conference, an organization operating in every southern state, with headquarters in Atlanta, Georgia. We have some eighty-five affiliated organizations across the South, and one of them is the Alabama Christian Movement for Human Rights. Frequently we share staff, educational and financial resources with our affiliates. Several months ago the affiliate here in Birmingham asked us to be on call to engage in a nonviolent direct-action program if such were deemed necessary. We readily consented, and when the hour came we lived up to our promise. So I, along with several members of my staff, am here because I was invited here. I am here because I have organizational ties here.

But more basically, I am in Birmingham because injustice is here. Just as the prophets of the eighth century B.C. left their villages and carried their "thus saith the Lord" far beyond the boundaries of their home towns, and just as the Apostle Paul left his village of Tarsus and carried the gospel of Jesus Christ to the far corners of the Greco-Roman world, so am I compelled to carry the gospel of freedom beyond my own home town. Like Paul, I must constantly respond to the Macedonian call for aid.

Moreover, I am cognizant of the interrelatedness of all communities and states. I cannot sit idly by in Atlanta and not be concerned about what happens in Birmingham. Injustice anywhere is a threat to justice everywhere. We are caught in an inescapable network of mutuality, tied in a single garment of destiny. Whatever affects one directly, affects all indirectly. Never again can we afford to live with the narrow, provincial "outside agitator" idea. Anyone who lives inside the United States can never be considered an outsider anywhere within its bounds.

You deplore the demonstrations taking place in Birmingham. But your statement, I am sorry to say, fails to express a similar concern for the conditions that brought about the demonstrations. I am sure that none of you would want to rest content with the superficial kind of social analysis that deals merely with effects and does not grapple with underlying causes. It is unfortunate that demonstrations are taking place in Birmingham, but it is even more unfortunate that the city's white power structure left the Negro community with no alternative.

In any nonviolent campaign there are four basic steps: collection of the facts to determine whether injustices exist; negotiation; self-purification; and direct action. We have gone through all these steps in Birmingham. There can be no gainsaying the fact that racial injustice engulfs this community. Birmingham is probably the most thoroughly segregated city in the United States. Its ugly record of brutality is widely known. Negroes have experienced grossly unjust treatment in the courts. There have been more unsolved bombings of Negro homes and churches in Birmingham than in any other city in the nation. These are the hard, brutal facts of the case. On the basis of these conditions, Negro leaders sought to negotiate with the city fathers. But the latter consistently refused to engage in good-faith negotiation . . . .

[Omitted here are three paragraphs describing unsuccessful negotiations with merchants to remove racial signs from stores, and strategies for timing the direct action campaign which followed.]

You may well ask: "Why direct action? Why sit-ins, marches and so forth? Isn't negotiation a better path?" You are quite right in calling for negotiation. Indeed, this is the very purpose of direct action.

Nonviolent direct action seeks to create such a crisis and foster such a tension that a community which has constantly refused to negotiate is forced to confront the issue. It seeks so to dramatize the issue that it can no longer be ignored. My citing the creation of tension as part of the work of the nonviolent-register may sound rather shocking. But I must confess that I am not afraid of the word "tension." I have earnestly opposed violent tension, but there is a type of constructive, non-violent tension which is necessary for growth. Just as Socrates felt that it was necessary to create a tension in the mind so that individuals could rise from the bondage of myths and half-truths to the unfettered realm of creative analysis and objective appraisal, so must we see the need for nonviolent gadflies to create the kind of tension in society that will help men rise from the dark depths of prejudice and racism to the majestic heights of understanding and brotherhood.

The purpose of our direct-action program is to create a situation so crisis-packed that it will inevitably open the door to negotiation. I therefore concur with you in your call for negotiation. Too long has our beloved Southland been bogged down in a tragic effort to live in monologue rather than dialogue.

One of the basic points in your statement is that the action that I and my associates have taken in Birmingham is untimely . . . . My friends, I must say to you that we have not made a single gain in civil rights without determined legal and nonviolent pressure. Lamentably, it is an historical fact that privileged groups seldom give up their privileges voluntarily. Individuals may see the moral light and voluntarily give up their unjust posture; but, as Reinhold Niebuhr has reminded us, groups tend to be more immoral than individuals.

We know through painful experience that freedom is never voluntarily given by the oppressor; it must be demanded by the oppressed. Frankly, I have yet to engage in a direct-action campaign that was "well timed" in the view of those who have not suffered unduly from the disease of segregation. For years now I have heard the word "Wait!" It rings in the ear of every Negro with piercing familiarity. This "Wait" has almost always meant "Never." We must come to see, with one of our distinguished jurists, that "justice too long delayed is justice denied."

We have waited for more than 340 years for our constitutional and God-given rights. The nations of Asia and Africa are moving with jetlike speed toward gaining political independence, but we still creep at horse-and-buggy pace toward gaining a cup of coffee at a lunch counter. Perhaps it is easy for those who have never felt the stinging darts of segregation to say, "Wait." But when you have seen vicious mobs lynch your mothers and fathers at will and drown your sisters and brothers at whim; when you have seen hate-filled policemen curse, kick and even kill your black brothers and sisters; when you see the vast majority of your twenty million Negro brothers smothering in an airtight cage of poverty in the midst of an affluent society; when you suddenly find your tongue twisted and your speech stammering as you seek to explain to your six-year-old daughter why she can't go to the public amusement park that has just been advertised on television, and see tears welling up in her eyes when she is told that Funtown is closed to colored children, and see ominous clouds of inferiority beginning to form in her little mental sky, and see her beginning to distort her personality by developing an unconscious bitterness toward white people; when you have to concoct an answer for a five-year-old son who is asking: "Daddy, why do white people treat colored people so mean?"; when you take a cross-country drive and find it necessary to sleep night after night in the uncomfortable corners of your automobile because no motel will accept you; when you are humiliated day in and day out by nagging signs reading "white" and "colored"; when your first name becomes "nigger," your middle name becomes "boy" (however old you are) and your last name becomes "John," and your wife and mother are never given the respected title "Mrs."; when you are harried by day and haunted by night by the fact that you are a Negro, living constantly at tiptoe stance, never quite knowing what to expect next, and are plagued with inner fears and outer resentments; when you are forever fighting a degenerating sense of "nobodiness"—then you will understand why we find it difficult to wait. There comes a time when the cup of endurance runs over, and men are no longer willing to be plunged into the abyss of despair. I hope, sirs, you can understand our legitimate and unavoidable impatience.

You express a great deal of anxiety over our willingness to break laws. This is certainly a legitimate concern. Since we so diligently urge people to obey the Supreme Court's decision of 1954 outlawing segregation in the public schools, at first glance it may seem rather paradoxical for us consciously to break laws. One may well ask: "How can you advocate breaking some laws and obeying others?" The answer lies in the fact that there are two types of laws: just and unjust. I would be the first to advocate obeying just laws. One has not only a legal but a moral responsibility to obey just laws. Conversely, one has a moral responsibility to disobey unjust laws. I would agree with St. Augustine that "an unjust law is no law at all."

Now, what is the difference between the two? How does one determine whether a law is just or unjust? A just law is a man-made code that squares with the moral law or the law of God. An unjust law is a code that is out of harmony with the moral law. To put it in the terms of St. Thomas Aquinas: An unjust law is a human law that is not rooted in eternal law and natural law. Any law that uplifts human personality is just. Any law that degrades human personality is unjust. All segregation statutes are unjust because segregation distorts the soul and damages the personality. It gives the segregator a false sense of superiority and the segregated a false sense of inferiority. Segregation, to use the terminology of the Jewish philosopher Martin Buber, substitutes an "I-it" relationship for an "I-thou" relationship and ends up relegating persons to the status of things. Hence segregation is not only politically, economically and sociologically unsound, it is morally wrong and sinful. Paul Tillich has said that sin is separation. Is not segregation an existential expression of man's tragic separation, his awful estrangement, his terrible sinfulness? Thus it is that I can urge men to obey the 1954 decision of the Supreme Court, for it is morally right; and I can urge them to disobey segregation ordinances, for they are morally wrong.

Let us consider a more concrete example of just and unjust laws. An unjust law is a code that a numerical or power majority group compels a minority group to obey but does not make binding on itself. This is *difference* made legal. By the same token, a just law is a code that a majority compels a minority to follow and that it is willing to follow itself. This is *sameness* made legal.

Let me give another explanation. A law is unjust if it is inflicted on a minority that, as a result of being denied the right to vote, had no part in enacting or devising the law. Who can say that the legislature of Alabama which set up that state's segregation laws was democratically elected? Throughout Alabama all sorts of devious methods are used to prevent Negroes from becoming registered voters, and there are some counties in which, even though Negroes constitute a majority of the population, not a single Negro is registered. Can any law enacted under such circumstances be considered democratically structured?

Sometimes a law is just on its face and unjust in its application. For instance, I have been arrested on a charge of parading without a permit. Now, there is nothing wrong in having an ordinance which requires a permit for a parade. But such an ordinance becomes unjust when it is used to maintain segregation and deny citizens the First-Amendment privilege of peaceful assembly and protest.

I hope you are able to see the distinction I am trying to point out. In no sense do I advocate evading or defying the law, as would the rabid segregationist. That would lead to anarchy. One who breaks an unjust law must do so openly, lovingly, and with a willingness to accept the penalty. I submit that an individual who breaks a law that conscience tells him is unjust, and who willingly accepts the penalty of imprisonment in order to arouse the conscience of the community over its injustice, is in reality expressing the highest respect for law.

Of course, there is nothing new about this kind of civil disobedience. It was evidenced sublimely in the refusal of Shadrach, Meshach and Abednego to obey the laws of Nebuchadnezzar, on the ground that a higher moral law was at stake. It was practiced superbly by the early Christians, who were willing to face hungry lions and the excruciating pain of chopping blocks rather than submit to certain unjust laws of the Roman Empire. To a degree, academic freedom is a reality today because Socrates practiced civil disobedience. In our own nation, the Boston Tea Party represented a massive act of civil disobedience.

We should never forget that everything Adolf Hitler did in Germany was "legal" and everything the Hungarian freedom fighters did in Hungary was "illegal." It was "illegal" to aid and comfort a Jew in Hitler's Germany. Even so, I am sure that, had I lived in Germany at the time, I would have aided and comforted my Jewish brothers. If today I lived in a Communist country where certain principles dear to the Christian faith are suppressed, I would openly advocate disobeying that country's anti-religious laws.

I must make two honest confessions to you, my Christian and Jewish brothers. First, I must confess that over the past few years I have been gravely disappointed with the white moderate. I have almost reached the regrettable conclusion that the Negro's great stumbling block in his stride toward freedom is not the White Citizen's Counciler or the Ku Klux Klanner, but the white moderate, who is more devoted to "order" than to justice; who prefers a negative peace which is the absence of tension to a positive peace which is the presence of justice; who constantly says: "I agree with you in the goal you seek, but I cannot agree with your methods of direct action"; who paternalistically believes he can set the timetable for another man's freedom; who lives by a mythical concept of time and who constantly advises the Negro to wait for a "more convenient season." Shallow understanding from people of good will is more frustrating than absolute misunderstanding from people of ill will. Lukewarm acceptance is much more bewildering than outright rejection.

I had hoped that the white moderate would understand that law and order exist for the purpose of establishing justice and that when they fail in this purpose they become the dangerously structured dams that block the flow of social progress. I had hoped that the white moderate would understand that the present tension in the South is a necessary phase of the transition from an obnoxious negative peace, in which the Negro passively accepted his unjust plight, to a substantive and positive peace, in which all men will respect the dignity and worth of human personality. Actually, we who engage in nonviolent direct action are not the creators of tension. We merely bring to the surface the hidden tension that is already alive. We bring it out in the open, where it can be seen and dealt with. Like a boil that can never be cured so long as it is covered up but must be opened with all its ugliness to the natural medicines of air and light, injustice must be exposed, with all the tension its exposure creates, to the light of human conscience and the air of national opinion before it can be cured.

In your statement you assert that our actions, even though peaceful, must be condemned because they precipitate violence. But is this a logical assertion? Isn't this like condemning a robbed man because his possession of money precipitated the evil act of robbery? Isn't this like condemning Socrates because his unswerving commitment to truth and his philosophical inquiries precipitated the act by the misguided populace in which they made him drink hemlock? Isn't this like condemning Jesus because his unique God-consciousness and never-ceasing devotion to God's will precipitated the evil act of crucifixion? We must come to see that, as the federal courts have consistently affirmed, it is wrong to urge an individual to cease his efforts to gain his basic constitutional rights because the quest may precipitate violence. Society must protect the robbed and punish the robber . . . .

[Omitted here is one paragraph expressing disappointed hope "that the white moderate would reject the myth of time"—i.e., the idea that man's lot inevitably improves, irrespective of actions performed for good or evil.]

You speak of our activity in Birmingham as extreme. At first I was rather disappointed that fellow clergymen would see my nonviolent efforts as those of an extremist. I began thinking about the fact that I stand in the middle of two opposing forces in the Negro community. One is a force of complacency, made up in part of Negroes who, as a result of long years of oppression, are so drained of self-respect and a sense of "somebodiness" that they have adjusted to segregation; and in part of a few middle-class Negroes who, because of a degree of academic and economic security and because in some ways they profit by segregation, have become insensitive to the problems of the masses. The other force is one of bitterness and hatred, and it comes perilously close to advocating violence. It is expressed in the various black nationalist groups that are springing up across the nation, the largest and best-known being Elijah Muhammad's Muslim movement. Nourished by the Negro's frustration over the continued existence of racial discrimination, this movement is made up of people who have lost faith in America, who have absolutely repudiated Christianity, and who have concluded that the white man is an incorrigible "devil."

I have tried to stand between these two forces, saying that we need emulate neither the "do-nothingism" of the complacent nor the hatred and despair of the black nationalist. For there is the more excellent way of love and nonviolent protest. I am grateful to God that, through the influence of the Negro church, the way of nonviolence became an integral part of our struggle.

If this philosophy had not emerged, by now many streets of the South would, I am convinced, be flowing with blood. And I am further convinced that if our white brothers dismiss as "rabble-rousers" and "outside agitators" those of us who employ nonviolent direct action, and if they refuse to support our nonviolent efforts, millions of Negroes will, out of frustration and despair, seek solace and security in black-nationalist ideologies—a development that would inevitably lead to a frightening racial nightmare.

Oppressed people cannot remain oppressed forever. The yearning for freedom eventually manifests itself, and that is what has happened to the American Negro. Something within has reminded him of his birthright of freedom, and something without has reminded him that it can be gained. Consciously or unconsciously, he has been caught up by the *Zeitgeist,* and with his black brothers of Africa and his brown and yellow brothers of Asia, South America and the Caribbean, the United States Negro is moving with a sense of great urgency toward the promised land of racial justice. If one recognizes this vital urge that has engulfed the Negro community, one should readily understand why public demonstrations are taking place. The Negro has many pent-up resentments and latent frustrations, and he must release them. So let him march; let him make prayer pilgrimages to the city hall; let him go on freedom rides—and try to understand why he must do so. If his repressed emotions are not released in nonviolent ways, they will seek expression through violence; this is not a threat but a fact of history. So I have not said to my people: "Get rid of your discontent." Rather, I have tried to say that this normal and healthy discontent can be channeled into the creative outlet of nonviolent direct action. And now this approach is being termed extremist.

But though I was initially disappointed at being categorized as an extremist, as I continued to think about the matter I gradually gained a measure of satisfaction from the label. Was not Jesus an extremist for love: "Love your enemies, bless them that curse you, do good to them that hate you, and pray for them which despitefully use you, and persecute you." Was not Amos an extremist for justice: "Let justice roll down like waters and righteousness like an ever-flowing stream." Was not Paul an extremist for the Christian gospel: "I bear in my body the marks of the Lord Jesus." Was not Martin Luther an extremist: "Here I stand; I cannot do otherwise, so help me God." And John Bunyan: "I will stay in jail to the end of my days before I make a butchery of my conscience." And Abraham Lincoln: "This nation cannot survive half slave and half free." And Thomas Jefferson: "We hold these truths to be self-evident, that all men are created equal . . . " So the question is not whether we will be extremists, but what kind of extremists we will be. Will we be extremists for hate or for love? Will we be extremists for the preservation of injustice or for the extension of justice? In that dramatic scene on Calvary's hill three men were crucified. We must never forget that all three were crucified for the same crime—the crime of extremism. Two were extremists for immorality, and thus fell below their environment. The other, Jesus Christ, was an extremist for love, truth and goodness, and thereby rose above his environment. Perhaps the South, the nation and the world are in dire need of creative extremists.

I had hoped that the white moderate would see this need. Perhaps I was too optimistic; perhaps I expected too much. I suppose I should have realized that few members of the oppressor race can understand the deep groans and passionate yearnings of the oppressed race, and still fewer have the vision to see that injustice must be rooted out by strong, persistent and determined action. I am thankful, however, that some of our white brothers in the South have grasped the meaning of this social revolution and committed themselves to it. They are still all too few in quantity, but they are big in quality. Some—such as Ralph McGill, Lillian Smith, Harry Golden, James McBride Dabbs, Ann Braden and Sarah Patton Boyle—have written about our struggle in eloquent and prophetic terms. Others have marched with us down nameless streets of the South. They have languished in filthy, roach-infested jails, suffering the abuse and brutality of policemen who view them as "dirty nigger-lovers." Unlike so many of their moderate brothers and sisters, they have recognized the urgency of the moment and sensed the need for powerful "action" antidotes to combat the disease of segregation . . . .

[Omitted here is King's second confession (see ¶ 20): eleven paragraphs expressing his dissatisfaction "with the white Church and its leadership."]

But even if the church does not come to the aid of justice, I have no despair about the future. I have no fear about the outcome of our struggle in Birmingham, even if our motives are at present misunderstood. We will reach the goal of freedom in Birmingham and all over the nation, because the goal of America is freedom. Abused and scorned though we may be, our destiny is tied up with America's destiny. Before the pilgrims landed at Plymouth, we were here. Before the pen of Jefferson etched the majestic words of the Declaration of Independence across the pages of history, we were here. For more than two centuries our forebears labored in this country without wages; they made cotton king; they built the homes of their masters while suffering gross injustice and shameful humiliation—and yet out of a bottomless vitality they continued to thrive and develop. If the inexpressible cruelties of slavery could not stop us, the opposition we now face will surely fail. We will win our freedom because the sacred heritage of our nation and the eternal will of God are embodied in our echoing demands.

Before closing I feel impelled to mention one other point in your statement that has troubled me profoundly. You warmly commended the Birmingham police force for keeping "order" and "preventing violence." I doubt that you would have so warmly commended the police force if you had seen its dogs sinking their teeth into unarmed, nonviolent Negroes. I doubt that you would so quickly commend the policemen if you were to observe their ugly and inhumane treatment of Negroes here in the city jail; if you were to watch them push and curse old Negro women and young Negro girls; if you were to see them slap and kick old Negro men and young boys; if you were to observe them, as they did on two occasions, refuse to give us food because we wanted to sing our grace together. I cannot join you in your praise of the Birmingham police department.

It is true that the police have exercised a degree of discipline in handling the demonstrators. In this sense they have conducted themselves rather "nonviolently" in public. But for what purpose? To preserve the evil system of segregation. Over the past few years I have consistently preached that nonviolence demands that the means we use must be as pure as the ends we seek. I have tried to make clear that it is wrong to use immoral means to attain moral ends. But now I must affirm that it is just as wrong, or perhaps even more so, to use moral means to preserve immoral ends . . . . As T. S. Eliot has said: "The last temptation is the greatest treason: To do the right deed for the wrong reason."

I wish you had commended the Negro sit-inners and demonstrators of Birmingham for their sublime courage, their willingness to suffer and their amazing discipline in the midst of great provocation. One day the South will recognize its real heroes. They will be the James Merediths, with the noble sense of purpose that enables them to face jeering and hostile mobs, and with the agonizing loneliness that characterizes the life of the pioneer. They will be old, oppressed, battered Negro women, symbolized in a seventy-two-year-old woman in Montgomery, Alabama, who rose up with a sense of dignity and with her people decided not to ride segregated buses, and who responded with ungrammatical profundity to one who inquired about her weariness: "My feets is tired, but my soul is at rest." They will be the young high school and college students, the young ministers of the gospel and a host of their elders, courageously and nonviolently sitting in at lunch counters and willingly going to jail for conscience' sake. One day the South will know that when these disinherited children of God sat down at lunch counters, they were in reality standing up for what is best in the American dream and for the most sacred values in our Judaeo-Christian heritage, thereby bringing our nation back to those great wells of democracy which were dug deep by the founding fathers in their formulation of the Constitution and the Declaration of Independence.

Never before have I written so long a letter. I'm afraid it is much too long to take your precious time. I can assure you that it would have been much shorter if I had been writing from a comfortable desk, but what else can one do when he is alone in a narrow jail cell, other than write long letters, think long thoughts and pray long prayers?

If I have said anything in this letter that overstates the truth and indicates an unreasonable impatience, I beg you to forgive me. If I have said anything that understates the truth and indicates my having a patience that allows me to settle for anything less than brotherhood, I beg God to forgive me.

I hope this letter finds you strong in faith. I also hope that circumstances will soon make it possible for me to meet each of you, not as an integrationist or a civil-rights leader but as a fellow clergyman and a Christian brother. Let us all hope that the dark clouds of racial prejudice will soon pass away and the deep fog of misunderstanding will be lifted from our fear-drenched communities, and in some not too distant tomorrow the radiant stars of love and brotherhood will shine over our great nation with all their scintillating beauty.

Yours for the cause of Peace and Brotherhood,

MARTIN LUTHER KING, JR.

STUDY QUESTIONS

1. To whom is King writing? What is the purpose of his letter?

2. King gives several reasons why he is justified in coming in as an "outsider" to lead demonstrations in Birmingham. What are his reasons? Are they valid ones in your opinion? What replies might his opponents have made to each?

3. Does King's description of the personal feelings of Negroes concerning their segregated status have any place in a purportedly reasoned statement such as this one? What is his purpose in including it? Did it have the effect on you that you think he intended?

4. To what highest authority is King appealing when he states: "A just law is a man-made code that squares with the moral law or the law of God"? How would *you* determine the difference between a just and an unjust law? Examine your answer to the preceding question and determine to what highest authority you were appealing.

5. King is using a mild form of irony when he states: "I suppose I should have realized that few members of the oppressor race can understand the deep groans and passionate yearnings of the oppressed race . . .". Where else does he employ irony? Do you think it is an effective tool in his argument?

6. Can you classify the overall tone of King's argument (for example, is it purely logical, sardonic, highly emotional, etc.)? Is the tone consistent throughout?

PART TWO

The Literature of Violence

6

From MAN'S FATE*

Andre Malraux

Andre Malraux is a famous French man of letters, political figure and adventurer. He was active in the revolution in China during 1925 and 1927, and in Spain (1935-1938) where he helped to organize the Loyalist air force. Recently he was Minister of Culture under de Gaulle. Among his most famous works are Man's Fate *(1934),* Man's Hope *(1938), and* The Voices of Silence *(1953).*

Man's Fate concerns the destiny and dignity of human beings in the revolutionary struggle of the communists against the Kuomintang of Chiang Kai-Shek during the 1920's. Ch'en Ta Erh, a graduate of a missionary school and now a terrorist, opens the novel with an act of violence. In this opening selection, Malraux depicts the feelings and struggles of the assassin at the climax of his act and shows us that even professional revolutionaries feel the dread of being alone with death.

March 21, 1927

Twelve-thirty midnight

SHOULD HE try to raise the mosquito-netting? Or should he strike through it? Ch'en was torn by anguish: he was sure of himself, yet at the moment he could feel nothing but bewilderment—his eyes riveted to the mass of white gauze that hung from the ceiling over a body less visible than a shadow, and from which emerged only that foot half-turned in sleep, yet living—human flesh.

The only light came from the neighboring building—a great rectangle of wan electric light cut by window-bars, one of which streaked

---

the bed just below the foot as if to stress its solidity and life.

Four or five klaxons screamed at once. Was he discovered?

Oh, what a relief to fight, to fight enemies who defend themselves, enemies who are awake!

The wave of uproar subsided: some traffic jam (there were still traffic jams out there in the world of men—). He found himself again facing the great soft smudge of gauze and the rectangle of light, both motionless in this night in which time no longer existed.

He repeated to himself that this man must die—stupidly, for he knew that he would kill him. Whether he was caught or not, executed or not, did not matter. Nothing existed but this foot, this man whom he must strike without letting him defend himself—for if he defended himself, he would cry out.

Ch'en was becoming aware, with a revulsion verging on nausea, that he stood here, not as a fighter, but as a sacrificial priest. He was serving the gods of his choice; but beneath his sacrifice to the Revolution lay a world of depths beside which this night of crushing anguish was bright as day. "To assassinate is not only to kill, alas . . ." In his pockets, his fumbling right hand clutched a folded razor, his left a short dagger. He thrust them as deeply as possible, as though the night did not suffice to hide his actions. The razor was surer, but Ch'en felt that he could never use it; the dagger disgusted him less. He let go the razor, the back of which pressed against his clenched fingers; the dagger was naked in his pocket. As he passed it over to his right hand, his left hand dropped against the wool of his sweater and remained glued to it. He raised his right arm slightly, petrified by the continued silence that surrounded him, as though he expected some unseen thing to topple over. But no—nothing happened: it was still up to him to act.

That foot lived like a sleeping animal. Was it attached to a body? "Am I going mad?" He had to see that body—see it, see that head. In order to do that—enter the area of light, let his squat shadow fall upon the bed.

What was the resistance of flesh? Convulsively, Ch'en pressed the point of the dagger into his left arm. The pain (he was no longer aware that it was his own arm), the certainty of torture if the sleeper were to awaken, released him for an instant: torture was better than this atmosphere of madness. He drew close. Yes, this was the man he had seen, two hours before, in broad daylight. The foot, which nearly touched Ch'en's trousers, suddenly turned like a key, then turned back to its position in the silent night. Perhaps the sleeper felt his presence, but not enough to wake up . . . Ch'en shuddered: an insect was running over his skin! No!—blood trickling down his arm. And still that seasick feeling.

One single motion, and the man would be dead. To kill him was nothing: touching him was the impossible. And it was imperative to stab with precision.

The sleeper, lying on his back in the European-style bed, was wearing only a pair of short drawers, but his ribs were not visible under the full flesh. Ch'en had to take the nipples as gauging points. He tried holding the dagger with the blade up. But the left breast was the one away from him: he would have to strike at arm's length through the mosquito-netting. He changed the position of the dagger: blade down. To touch this motionless body was as difficult as to stab a corpse, perhaps for the same reason. As if called forth by this notion of a corpse, a grating sound suddenly issued from the man's throat. Ch'en could no longer even draw back, for his legs and arms had gone completely limp. But the rattle became regular: the man was not dying, he was snoring. He again became living, vulnerable; and at the same time, Ch'en felt himself ridiculed. The body turned gently towards the right. Was he going to wake up now? With a blow that would have split a plank Ch'en struck through the gauze. Sensitive to the very tip of the blade, he felt the body rebound towards him, flung up by the springs of the bed. He stiffened his arm furiously to hold it down: like severed halves drawn to each other, the legs sprang together toward the chest; then they jerked out, straight and stiff. Ch'en should have struck again—but how was he to withdraw the dagger? The body, still on its side, was unstable, and instead of being reassured by the convulsion which had just shaken it, Ch'en had the impression of pinning it down to the bed with this short blade on which his whole weight rested.

Through the great gash in the mosquito-netting, he could see very clearly; the eyelids open—had he been able to wake up?—the eyeballs white. Around the dagger the blood was beginning to flow, black in that deceptive light. In its balanced weight the body still held life. Ch'en could not let go the handle. A current of unbearable anguish passed between the corpse and himself, through the dagger, his stiffened arm, his aching shoulder, to the very depth of his chest, to his convulsive heart—the only moving thing in the room. He was utterly motionless; the blood that continued to flow from his left arm seemed to be that of the man on the bed. Although outwardly nothing had happened, he was suddenly certain that this man was dead. Scarcely breathing, he held the corpse down—as firmly as ever—on its side—held it thus in the dim motionless light, in the solitude of the room.

Nothing bore witness to the struggle—not even the tear in the gauze, which seemed to have been divided into two strips—nothing but the silence and the over-powering intoxication into which he was sinking. Cut off from the world of the living, he clung to his dagger. His grip became increasingly tighter, but his arm-muscles relaxed and his entire arm began to tremble. It was not fear—it was a dread at once horrible and solemn, which he had not experienced since childhood: he was alone with death, alone in a place without men, limply crushed by horror and by the taste of blood.

• • •

STUDY QUESTIONS

1. Explain the following statements by Ch'en:
   a. "Oh what a relief to fight, to fight enemies who defend themselves, enemies who are awake!"
   b. "To assassinate is not only to kill . . .".
   c. "To kill him was nothing: touching him was impossible."
2. Enumerate the emotions that run through Ch'en before he kills.
3. What is Ch'en's immediate reaction to the killings?
4. Why does Ch'en press the dagger into his own arm? What is the effect on his thought when he does this?
5. Why did Ch'en feel himself "ridiculed" when the victim begins to snore?
6. Is revolutionary or political assassination ever justified? Explain.

7

THE PRUSSIAN OFFICER*

D. H. Lawrence

Son of a Nottingham coal miner, D. H. Lawrence is now considered to be a major writer of our century. His first novel, The White Peacock, *was published in 1911 when he was 26 years old; it was followed by* Sons and Lovers *two years later. The* Rainbow *(1915) and* Women in Love *(1921) reinforced his reputation. Concerned with the profound ramifications of love and sex, he created a sensation in 1928 with* Lady Chatterley's Lover. *Lawrence died of tuberculosis in France in 1930 after a long illness. "The Prussian Officer" was written in 1914 after he had married Frieda von Richthofen and had stayed with her family at a garrison town in Germany.*

In "The Prussian Officer" Lawrence explores the psychological relationship between a captain and his orderly as they are inevitably drawn into a vortex of violence and disaster.

THEY HAD marched more than thirty kilometres since dawn, along the white, hot road where occasional thickets of trees threw a moment of shade, then out into the glare again. On either hand, the valley, wide and shallow, glittered with heat; dark green patches of rye, pale young corn, fallow and meadow and black pine woods spread in a dull, hot diagram under a glistening sky. But right in front the mountains ranged across, pale blue and very still, snow gleaming gently out of the deep atmosphere. And towards the mountains, on and on, the regiment marched between the rye fields and the meadows, between the scraggy fruit trees set regularly on either side the high road. The burnished, dark green rye threw off a suffocating heat, the mountains drew gradually nearer and more distinct. While the feet of the soldiers grew hotter, sweat ran through their hair under their helmets, and their

*From THE COMPLETE SHORT STORIES OF D. H. LAWRENCE, Volume I. Reprinted by permission of The Viking Press, Inc.

knapsacks could burn no more in contact with their shoulders, but seemed instead to give off a cold, prickly sensation.

He walked on and on in silence, staring at the mountains ahead, that rose sheer out of the land and stood fold behind fold, half earth, half heaven, the heaven, the barrier with slits of soft snow, in the pale, bluish peaks.

He could now walk almost without pain. At the start, he had determined not to limp. It had made him sick to take the first steps, and during the first mile or so, he had compressed his breath, and the cold drops of sweat had stood on his forehead. But he had walked it off. What were they after all but bruises! He had looked at them, as he was getting up: deep bruises on the backs of his thighs. And since he had made his first step in the morning, he had been conscious of them, till now he had a tight, hot place in his chest, with suppressing the pain, and holding himself in. There seemed no air when he breathed. But he walked almost lightly.

The Captain's hand had trembled at taking his coffee at dawn: his orderly saw it again. And he saw the fine figure of the Captain wheeling on horseback at the farmhouse ahead, a handsome figure in pale blue uniform with facings of scarlet, and the metal gleaming on the black helmet and the sword-scabbard, and dark streaks of sweat coming on the silky bay horse. The orderly felt he was connected with that figure moving so suddenly on horseback: he followed it like a shadow, mute and inevitable and damned by it. And the officer was always aware of the tramp of the company behind, the march of his orderly among the men.

The Captain was a tall man of about forty, grey at the temples. He had a handsome, finely knit figure, and was one of the best horsemen in the West. His orderly, having to rub him down, admired the amazing riding-muscles of his loins.

For the rest, the orderly scarcely noticed the officer any more than he noticed himself. It was rarely he saw his master's face: he did not look at it. The Captain had reddish-brown, stiff hair that he wore short upon his skull. His moustache was also cut short and bristly over a full, brutal mouth. His face was rather rugged, the cheeks thin. Perhaps the man was the more handsome for the deep lines in his face, the irritable tension of his brow, which gave him the look of a man who fights with life. His fair eyebrows stood bushy over light blue eyes that were always flashing with cold fire.

He was a Prussian aristocrat, haughty and overbearing. But his mother had been a Polish Countess. Having made too many gambling debts when he was young, he had ruined his prospects in the Army, and remained an infantry captain. He had never married: his position did not allow of it, and no woman had ever moved him to it. His time he spent riding—occasionally he rode one of his own horses at the races— and at the officers' club. Now and then he took himself a mistress. But after such an event, he returned to duty with his brow still more tense, his eyes still more hostile and irritable. With the men, however, he was merely impersonal, though a devil when roused; so that, on the whole, they feared him, but had no great aversion from him. They accepted him as the inevitable.

To his orderly he was at first cold and just and indifferent: he did not fuss over trifles. So that his servant knew practically nothing about him, except just what orders he would give, and how he wanted them obeyed. That was quite simple. Then the change gradually came.

The orderly was a youth of about twenty-two, of medium height, and well built. He had strong, heavy limbs, was swarthy, with a soft, black, young moustache. There was something altogether warm and young about him. He had firmly marked eye-brows over dark, expressionless eyes that seemed never to have thought, only to have received life direct through his senses, and acted straight from instinct.

Gradually the officer had become aware of his servant's young, vigorous, unconscious presence about him. He could not get away from the sense of the youth's person, while he was in attendance. It was like a warm flame upon the older man's tense, rigid body, that had become almost unliving, fixed. There was something in the young fellow's movement, that made the officer aware of him. And this irritated the Prussian. He did not choose to be touched into life by his servant. He might easily have changed his man, but he did not. He now very rarely looked direct at his orderly, but kept his face averted, as if to avoid seeing him. And yet as the young soldier moved unthinking about the apartment, the elder watched him, and would notice the movement of his strong young shoulders under the blue cloth, the bend of his neck. And it irritated him. To see the soldier's young, brown, shapely peasant's hand grasp the loaf or the wine-bottle sent a flash of hate or of anger through the elder man's blood. It was not that the youth was clumsy: it was rather the blind, instinctive sureness of movement of an unhampered young animal that irritated the officer to such a degree.

Once, when a bottle of wine had gone over, and the red gushed out on to the tablecloth, the officer had started up with an oath, and his eyes, bluey like fire, had held those of the confused youth for a moment. It was a shock for the young soldier. He felt something sink deeper, deeper into his soul, where nothing had ever gone before. It left him rather blank and wondering. Some of his natural completeness in himself was gone, a little uneasiness took its place. And from that time an undiscovered feeling had held between the two men.

Henceforward the orderly was afraid of really meeting his master. His subconsciousness remembered those steely blue eyes and the harsh brows, and did not intend to meet them again. So he always stared past his master and avoided him. Also, in a little anxiety, he waited for the three months to have gone, when his time would be up. He began to feel a constraint in the Captain's presence, and the soldier even more than the officer wanted to be left alone, in his neutrality as servant.

He had served the Captain for more than a year, and knew his duty. This he performed easily, as if it were natural to him. The officer and his commands he took for granted, as he took the sun and the rain, and he served as a matter of course. It did not implicate him personally.

But now if he were going to be forced into a personal interchange with his master he would be like a wild thing caught, he felt he must get away.

But the influence of the young soldier's being had penetrated through the officer's stiffened discipline, and perturbed the man in him. He, however, was a gentleman, with long, fine hands and cultivated movements, and was not going to allow such a thing as the stirring of his innate self. He was a man of passionate temper, who had always kept himself suppressed. Occasionally there had been a duel, an out-burst before the soldiers. He knew himself to be always on the point of breaking out. But he kept himself hard to the idea of the Service. Whereas the young soldier seemed to live out his warm, full nature, to give it off in his very movements, which had a certain zest, such as wild animals have in free movement. And this irritated the officer more and more.

In spite of himself, the Captain could not regain his neutrality of feeling towards his orderly. Nor could he leave the man alone. In spite of himself, he watched him, gave him sharp orders, tried to take up as much of his time as possible. Sometimes he flew into a rage with the young soldier, and bullied him. Then the orderly shut himself off, as it were out of earshot, and waited, with sullen, flushed face, for the end of the noise. The words never pierced to his intelligence, he made himself, protectively, impervious to the feelings of his master.

He had a scar on his left thumb, a deep seam going across the knuckle. The officer had long suffered from it, and wanted to do something to it. Still it was there, ugly and brutal on the young, brown hand. At last the Captain's reserve gave way. One day, as the orderly was smoothing out the tablecloth, the officer pinned down his thumb with a pencil, asking:

"How did you come by that?"

The young man winced and drew back at attention.

"A wood axe, Herr Hauptmann," he answered.

The officer waited for further explanation. None came. The orderly went about his duties. The elder man was sullenly angry. His servant avoided him. And the next day he had to use all his will-power to avoid seeing the scarred thumb. He wanted to get hold of it and—A hot flame ran in his blood.

He knew his servant would soon be free, and would be glad. As yet, the soldier had held himself off from the elder man. The Captain grew madly irritable. He could not rest when the soldier was away, and when he was present, he glared at him with tormented eyes. He hated those fine black brows over the unmeaning dark eyes, he was infuriated by the free movement of the handsome limbs, which no military discipline could make stiff. And he became harsh and cruelly bullying, using contempt and satire. The young soldier only grew more mute and expressionless.

"What cattle were you bred by, that you can't keep straight eyes? Look me in the eyes when I speak to you."

And the soldier turned his dark eyes to the other's face, but there was no sight in them: he stared with the slightest possible cast, holding back his sight, perceiving the blue of his master's eyes, but receiving no look from them. And the elder man went pale, and his reddish eyebrows twitched. He gave his order, barrenly.

Once he flung a heavy military glove into the young soldier's face. Then he had the satisfaction of seeing the black eyes flare up into his own, like a blaze when straw is thrown on a fire. And he had laughed with a little tremor and a sneer.

But there were only two months more. The youth instinctively tried to keep himself intact: he tried to serve the officer as if the latter were an abstract authority and not a man. All his instinct was to avoid personal contact, even definite hate. But in spite of himself the hate grew, responsive to the officer's passion. However, he put it in the background. When he had left the Army he could dare acknowledge it. By nature he was active, and had many friends. He thought what amazing good fellows they were. But, without knowing it, he was alone. Now this solitariness was intensified. It would carry him through his term. But the officer seemed to be going irritably insane, and the youth was deeply frightened.

The soldier had a sweetheart, a girl from the mountains, independent and primitive. The two walked together, rather silently. He went with her, not to talk, but to have his arm round her, and for the physical contact. This eased him, made it easier for him to ignore the Captain; for he could rest with her held fast against his chest. And she, in some unspoken fashion, was there for him. They loved each other.

The Captain perceived it, and was mad with irritation. He kept the young man engaged all the evenings long, and took pleasure in the dark look that came on his face. Occasionally, the eyes of the two men met, those of the younger sullen and dark, doggedly unalterable, those of the elder sneering with restless contempt.

The officer tried hard not to admit the passion that had got hold of him. He would not know that his feeling for his orderly was anything but that of a man incensed by his stupid, perverse servant. So, keeping quite justified and conventional in his consciousness, he let the other thing run on. His nerves, however, were suffering. At last he slung the end of a belt in his servant's face. When he saw the youth start back, the pain-tears in his eyes and the blood on his mouth he had felt at once a thrill of deep pleasure and of shame.

But this, he acknowledged to himself, was a thing he had never done before. The fellow was too exasperating. His own nerves must be going to pieces. He went away for some days with a woman.

It was a mockery of pleasure. He simply did not want the woman. But he stayed on for his time. At the end of it, he came back in an agony of irritation, torment, and misery. He rode all the evening, then came straight into supper. His orderly was out. The officer sat with his long, fine hands lying on the table, perfectly still, and all his blood seemed to be corroding.

At last his servant entered. He watched the strong, easy young figure, the fine eyebrows, the thick black hair. In a week's time the youth had got back his old well-being. The hands of the officer twitched and seemed to be full of mad flame. The young man stood at attention, unmoving, shut off.

The meal went in silence. But the orderly seemed eager. He made a clatter with the dishes.

"Are you in a hurry?" asked the officer, watching the intent, warm face of his servant. The other did not reply.

"Will you answer my question?" said the Captain.

"Yes, sir," replied the orderly, standing with his pile of deep Army plates. The Captain waited, looked at him, then asked again:

"Are you in a hurry?"

"Yes, sir," came the answer, that sent a flash through the listener.

"For what?"

"I was going out, sir."

"I want you this evening."

There was a moment's hesitation. The officer had a curious stiffness of countenance.

"Yes, sir," replied the servant, in his throat.

"I want you tomorrow evening also—in fact, you may consider your evenings occupied, unless I give you leave."

The mouth with the young moustache set close.

"Yes, sir," answered the orderly, loosening his lips for a moment.

He again turned to the door.

"And why have you a piece of pencil in your ear?"

The orderly hesitated, then continued on his way without answering. He set the plates in a pile outside the door, took the stump of pencil from his ear, and put it in his pocket. He had been copying a verse for his sweetheart's birthday card. He returned to finish clearing the table. The officer's eyes were dancing, he had a little, eager smile.

"Why have you a piece of pencil in your ear?" he asked.

The orderly took his hands full of dishes. His master was standing near the great green stove, a little smile on his face, his chin thrust forward. When the young soldier saw him his heart suddenly ran hot.

He felt blind. Instead of answering, he turned dazedly to the door. As he was crouching to set down the dishes, he was pitched forward by a kick from behind. The pots went in a stream down the stairs, he clung to the pillar of the banisters. And as he was rising he was kicked heavily again, and again, so that he clung sickly to the post for some moments. His master had gone swiftly into the room and closed the door. The maid-servant downstairs looked up the staircase and made a mocking face at the crockery disaster.

The officer's heart was plunging. He poured himself a glass of wine, part of which he spilled on the floor, and gulped the remainder, leaning against the cool, green stove. He heard his man collecting the dishes from the stairs. Pale, as if intoxicated, he waited. The servant entered again. The Captain's heart gave a pang, as of pleasure, seeing the young fellow bewildered and uncertain on his feet, with pain.

"Schoner!" he said.

The soldier was a little slower in coming to attention.

"Yes, sir!"

The youth stood before him, with pathetic young moustache, and fine eyebrows very distinct on his forehead of dark marble.

"I asked you a question."

"Yes, sir."

The officer's tone bit like acid.

"Why had you a pencil in your ear?"

Again the servant's heart ran hot, and he could not breathe. With dark, strained eyes, he looked at the officer, as if fascinated. And he stood there sturdily planted, unconscious. The withering smile came into the Captain's eyes, and he lifted his foot.

"I—I forgot it—sir," panted the soldier, his dark eyes fixed on the other man's dancing blue ones.

"What was it doing there?"

He saw the young man's breast heaving as he made an effort for words.

"I had been writing."

"Writing what?"

Again the soldier looked him up and down. The officer could hear him panting. The smile came into the blue eyes. The soldier worked his dry throat, but could not speak. Suddenly the smile lit like a flame on the officer's face, and a kick came heavily against the orderly's thigh.

The youth moved a pace sideways. His face went dead, with two black, staring eyes.

"Well?" said the officer.

The orderly's mouth had gone dry, and his tongue rubbed in it as on dry brown-paper. He worked his throat. The officer raised his foot. The servant went stiff.

"Some poetry, sir," came the crackling, unrecognizable sound of his voice.

"Poetry, what poetry?" asked the Captain, with a sickly smile.

Again there was the working in the throat. The Captain's heart had suddenly gone down heavily, and he stood sick and tired.

"For my girl, sir," he heard the dry, inhuman sound.

"Oh!" he said, turning away. "Clear the table."

"Click!" went the soldier's throat; then again, "Click!" and then the half-articulate:

"Yes, sir."

The young soldier was gone, looking old, and walking heavily.

The officer, left alone, held himself rigid, to prevent himself from thinking. His instinct warned him that he must not think. Deep inside him was the intense gratification of his passion, still working powerfully. Then there was a counter-action, a horrible breaking down of something inside him, a whole agony of reaction. He stood there for an hour motionless, a chaos of sensations, but rigid with a will to keep blank his consciousness, to prevent his mind grasping. And he held himself so until the worst of the stress had passed, when he began to drink, drank himself to an intoxication, till he slept obliterated. When he woke in the morning he was shaken to the base of his nature. But he fought off the realization of what he had done. He had prevented his mind from taking it in, had suppressed it along with his instincts, and the conscious man had nothing to do with it. He felt only as after a bout of intoxication, weak, but the affair itself all dim and not to be recovered. Of the drunkenness of his passion he successfully refused remembrance. And when his orderly appeared with coffee, the officer assumed the same self he had had the morning before. He refused the event of the past night—denied it had ever been—and was successful in his denial. He had not done any such thing—not he himself. Whatever there might be, lay at the door of a stupid, insubordinate servant.

The orderly had gone about in a stupor all the evening. He drank some beer because he was parched, but not much, the alcohol made his feeling come back, and he could not bear it. He was dulled, as if nine-tenths of the ordinary man in him were inert. He crawled about disfigured. Still, when he thought of the kicks, he went sick, and when he thought of the threat of more kicking, in the room afterwards, his heart went hot and faint, and he panted, remembering the one that had come. He had been forced to say, "For my girl." He was much too done even to want to cry. His mouth hung slightly open, like an idiot's. He felt vacant, and wasted. So, he wandered at his work, painfully, and very slowly and clumsily, fumbling blindly with the brushes, and finding it difficult, when he sat down, to summon the energy to move again. His limbs, his jaw, were slack and nerveless. But he was very tired. He got to bed at last, and slept inert, relaxed, in a sleep that was rather stupor than slumber, a dead night of stupefaction shot through with gleams of anguish.

In the morning were the manoeuvres. But he woke even before the bugle sounded. The painful ache in his chest, the dryness of his throat, the awful steady feeling of misery made his eyes come awake and dreary at once. He knew, without thinking, what had happened. And he knew that the day had come again, when he must go on with his round. The last bit of darkness was being pushed out of the room. He would have to move his inert body and go on. He was so young, and had known so little trouble, that he was bewildered. He only wished it would stay night, so that he could lie still, covered up by the darkness. And yet nothing would prevent the day from coming, nothing would save him from having to get up and saddle the Captain's horse, and make the Captain's coffee. It was there, inevitable. And then, he thought, it was impossible. Yet they would not leave him free. He must go and take the coffee to the Captain. He was too stunned to understand it. He only knew it was inevitable—inevitable, however long he lay inert.

At last, after heaving at himself, for he seemed to be a mass of inertia, he got up. But he had to force every one of his movements from behind, with his will. He felt lost, and dazed, and helpless. Then he clutched hold of the bed, the pain was so keen. And looking at his thighs, he saw the darker bruises on his swarthy flesh and he knew that, if he pressed one of his fingers on one of the bruises, he should faint. But he did not want to faint—he did not want anybody to know. No one should ever know. It was between him and the Captain. There were only the two people in the world now—himself and the Captain.

Slowly, economically, he got dressed and forced himself to walk. Everything was obscure, except just what he had his hands on. But he managed to get through his work. The very pain revived his dull senses. The worst remained yet. He took the tray and went up to the Captain's room. The officer, pale and heavy, sat at the table. The orderly, as he saluted, felt himself put out of existence. He stood still for a moment submitting to his own nullification—then he gathered himself, seemed to regain himself, and then the Captain began to grow vague, unreal, and the younger soldier's heart beat up. He clung to this situation—that the Captain did not exist—so that he himself might live. But when he saw his officer's hand tremble as he took the coffee, he felt everything falling shattered. And he went away, feeling as if he himself were coming to pieces, disintegrated. And when the Captain was there on horseback, giving orders, while he himself stood, with rifle and knapsack, sick with pain, he felt as if he must shut his eyes—as if he must shut his eyes on everything. It was only the long agony of marching with a parched throat that filled him with one single, sleep-heavy intention: to save himself.

II

He was getting used even to his parched throat. That the snowy peaks were radiant among the sky, that the whitey-green glacier-river twisted through its pale shoals in the valley below, seemed almost supernatural. But he was going mad with fever and thirst. He plodded on uncomplaining. He did not want to speak, not to anybody. There were two gulls, like flakes of water and snow, over the river. The scent of green rye soaked in sunshine came like a sickness. And the march continued, monotonously, almost like a bad sleep.

At the next farm-house, which stood low and broad near the high road, tubs of water had been put out. The soldiers clustered round to drink. They took off their helmets, and the steam mounted from their wet hair. The Captain sat on horseback, watching. He needed to see his orderly. His helmet threw a dark shadow over his light, fierce eyes, but his moustache and mouth and chin were distinct in the sunshine. The orderly must move under the presence of the figure of the horseman. It was not that he was afraid, or cowed. It was as if he was disembowelled, made empty, like an empty shell. He felt himself as nothing, a shadow creeping under the sunshine. And, thirsty as he was, he could scarcely drink, feeling the Captain near him. He would not take off his helmet to wipe his wet hair. He wanted to stay in shadow, not to be forced into consciousness. Starting, he saw the light heel of the officer prick the belly of the horse; the Captain cantered away, and he himself could relapse into vacancy.

Nothing, however, could give him back his living place in the hot, bright morning. He felt like a gap among it all. Whereas the Captain was prouder, overriding. A hot flash went through the young servant's body. The Captain was firmer and prouder with life, he himself was empty as a shadow. Again the flash went through him, dazing him out. But his heart ran a little firmer.

The company turned up the hill, to make a loop for the return. Below, from among the trees, the farm-bell clanged. He saw the labourers, mowing barefoot at the thick grass, leave off their work and go downhill, their scythes hanging over their shoulders, like long, bright claws curving down behind them. They seemed like dream-people, as if they had no relation to himself. He felt as in a blackish dream: as if all the other things were .there and had form, but he himself was only a consciousness, a gap that could think and perceive.

The soldiers were tramping silently up the glaring hillside. Gradually his head began to revolve, slowly, rhythmically. Sometimes it was dark before his eyes, as if he saw this world through a smoked glass, frail shadows and unreal. It gave him a pain in his head to walk.

The air was too scented, it gave no breath. All the lush green-stuff seemed to be issuing its sap, till the air was deathly, sickly with the smell of greenness. There was the perfume of clover, like pure honey and bees. Then there grew a faint acrid tang—they were near the beeches; and then a queer clattering noise, and a suffocating, hideous smell; they were passing a flock of sheep, a shepherd in a black smock, holding his crook. Why should the sheep huddle together under this fierce sun? He felt that the shepherd would not see him, though he could see the shepherd.

At last there was the halt. They stacked rifles in a conical stack, put down their kit in a scattered circle around it, and dispersed a little, sitting on a small knoll high on the hillside. The chatter began. The soldiers were steaming with heat, but were lively. He sat still, seeing the blue mountains rising upon the land, twenty kilometres away. There was a blue fold in the ranges, then out of that, at the foot, the broad, pale bed of the river, stretches of white-green water between pinkish-grey shoals among the dark pine woods. There it was, spread out a long way off. And it seemed to come downhill, the river. There was a raft being steered, a mile away. It was a strange country. Nearer, a red-roofed, broad farm with white base and square dots of windows crouched beside the wall of beech foliage on the wood's edge. There were long strips of rye and clover and pale green corn. And just at his feet, below the knoll, was a darkish bog, where globe flowers stood breathless still on their slim stalks. And some of the pale gold bubbles were burst, and a broken fragment hung in the air. He thought he was going to sleep.

Suddenly something moved into this coloured mirage before his eyes. The Captain, a small, light-blue and scarlet figure, was trotting evenly between the strips of corn, along the level brow of the hill. And the man making flag-signals was coming on. Proud and sure moved the horseman's figure, the quick, bright thing, in which was concentrated all the light of this morning, which for the rest lay a fragile, shining shadow. Submissive, apathetic, the young soldier sat and stared. But as the horse slowed to a walk, coming up the last steep path, the great flash flared over the body and soul of the orderly. He sat waiting. The back of his head felt as if it were weighted with a heavy piece of fire. He did not want to eat. His hands trembled slightly as he moved them. Meanwhile the officer on horseback was approaching slowly and proudly. The tension grew in the orderly's soul. Then again, seeing the Captain ease himself on the saddle, the flash blazed through him.

The Captain looked at the patch of light blue and scarlet, and dark heads, scattered closely on the hill-side. It pleased him. The command pleased him. And he was feeling proud. His orderly was among them in common subjection. The officer rose a little on his stirrups to look. The young soldier sat with averted, dumb face. The Captain relaxed on his seat. His slim-legged, beautiful horse, brown as a beechnut, walked proudly uphill. The Captain passed into the zone of the company's atmosphere: a hot smell of men, of sweat, of leather. He knew it very well. After a word with the lieutenant, he went a few paces higher, and sat there, a dominant figure, his sweat-marked horse swishing its tail, while he looked down on his men, on his orderly, a nonentity among the crowd.

The young soldier's heart was like fire in his chest, and he breathed with difficulty. The officer, looking downhill, saw three of the young soldiers, two pails of water between them, staggering across a sunny green field. A table had been set up under a tree, and there the slim lieutenant stood, importantly busy. Then the Captain summoned himself to an act of courage. He called his orderly.

The flame leapt into the young soldier's throat as he heard the command, and he rose blindly, stifled. He saluted, standing below the officer. He did not look up. But there was the flicker in the Captain's voice.

"Go to the inn and fetch me . . ." the officer gave his commands. "Quick!" he added.

At the last word, the heart of the servant leapt with a flash, and he felt the strength come over his body. But he turned in mechanical obedience, and set off at a heavy run downhill, looking almost like a bear, his trousers bagging over his military boots. And the officer watched this blind, plunging run all the way.

But it was only the outside of the orderly's body that was obeying so humbling and mechanically. Inside had gradually accumulated a core into which all the energy of that young life was compact and concentrated. He executed his commission, and plodded quickly back uphill. There was a pain in his head, as he walked, that made him twist his features unknowingly. But hard there in the centre of his chest was himself, himself, firm, and not to be plucked to pieces.

The Captain had gone up into the wood. The orderly plodded through the hot, powerfully smelling zone of the company's atmosphere. He had a curious mass of energy inside him now. The Captain was less real than himself. He approached the green entrance to the wood. There, in the half-shade, he saw the horse standing, the sunshine and the flickering shadow of leaves dancing over his brown body. There was a clearing where timber had lately been felled. Here, in the gold-green shade beside the brilliant cup of sunshine, stood two figures, blue and pink, the bits of pink showing out plainly. The Captain was talking to his lieutenant.

The orderly stood on the edge of the bright clearing, where great trunks of trees, stripped and glistening, lay stretched like naked, brown-skinned bodies. Chips of wood littered the trampled floor, like splashed light, and the bases of the felled trees stood here and there, with their raw, level tops. Beyond was the brilliant, sunlit green of a beech.

"Then I will ride forward," the orderly heard his Captain say. The lieutenant saluted and strode away. He himself went forward. A hot flash passed through his belly, as he tramped towards his officer.

The Captain watched the rather heavy figure of the young soldier stumble foward, and his veins, too, ran hot. This was to be man to man between them. He yielded before the solid, stumbling figure with bent head. The orderly stooped and put the food on a level-sawn tree-base. The Captain watched the glistening, sun-inflamed, naked hands. He wanted to speak to the young soldier but could not. The servant propped a bottle against his thigh, pressed open the cork, and poured out the beer into the mug. He kept his head bent. The Captain accepted the mug.

"Hot!" he said, as if amiably.

The flame sprang out of the orderly's heart, nearly suffocating him.

"Yes, sir," he replied, between shut teeth.

And he heard the sound of the Captain's drinking, and he clenched his fists, such a strong torment came into his wrists. Then came the faint clang of the closing of the pot-lid. He looked up. The Captain was watching him. He glanced swiftly away. Then he saw the officer stoop and take a piece of bread from the tree-base. Again the flash of flame went through the young soldier, seeing the stiff body stoop beneath him, and his hands jerked. He looked away. He could feel the officer was nervous. The bread fell as it was being broken. The officer ate the other piece. The two men stood tense and still, the master laboriously chewing his bread, the servant staring with averted face, his fist clenched.

Then the young soldier started. The officer had pressed open the lid of the mug again. The orderly watched the lid of the mug, and the white hand that clenched the handle, as if he were fascinated. It was raised. The youth followed it with his eyes. And then he saw the thin, strong throat of the elder man moving up and down as he drank, the strong jaw working. And the instinct which had been jerking at the young man's wrists suddenly jerked free. He jumped, feeling as if it were rent in two by a strong flame.

The spur of the officer caught in a tree-root, he went down backwards with a crash, the middle of his back thudding sickeningly against a sharp-edged tree-base, the pot flying away. And in a second the orderly, with serious, earnest young face, and underlip between his teeth, had got his knee in the officer's chest and was pressing the chin backward over the farther edge of the tree-stump, pressing, with all his heart behind in a passion of relief, the tension of his wrists exquisite with relief. And with the base of his palms he shoved at the chin, with all his might. And it was pleasant, too, to have that chin, that hard jaw already slightly rough with beard, in his hands. He did not relax one hair's breadth, but, all the force of all his blood exulting in his thrust, he shoved back the head of the other man, till there was a little "cluck" and a crunching sensation. Then he felt as if his head went to vapour. Heavy convulsions shook the body of the officer, frightening and horrifying the young soldier. Yet it pleased him, too, to repress them. It pleased him to keep his hands pressing back the chin, to feel the chest of the other man yield in expiration to the weight of his strong, young knees, to feel the hard twitchings of the prostrate body jerking his own whole frame, which was pressed down on it.

But it went still. He could look into the nostrils of the other man, the eyes he could scarcely see. How curiously the mouth was pushed out, exaggerating the full lips, and the moustache bristling up from them. Then, with a start, he noticed the nostrils gradually filled with blood. The red brimmed, hesitated, ran over, and went in a thin trickle down the face to the eyes.

It shocked and distressed him. Slowly, he got up. The body twitched and sprawled there, inert. He stood and looked at it in silence. It was a pity *it* was broken. It represented more than the thing which had kicked and bullied him. He was afraid to look at the eyes. They were hideous now, only the whites showing, and the blood running to them. The face of the orderly was drawn with horror at the sight. Well, it was so. In his heart he was satisfied. He had hated the face of the Captain. It was extinguished now. There was a heavy relief in the orderly's soul. That was as it should be. But he could not bear to see the long, military body lying broken over the tree-base, the fine fingers crisped. He wanted to hide it away.

Quickly, busily, he gathered it up and pushed it under the felled tree-trunks, which rested their beautiful, smooth length either end on logs. The face was horrible with blood. He covered it with the helmet. Then he pushed the limbs straight and decent, and brushed the dead leaves off the fine cloth of the uniform. So, it lay quite still in the shadow under there. A little strip of sunshine ran along the breast, from a chink between the logs. The orderly sat by it for a few moments. Here his own life also ended.

Then, through his daze, he heard the lieutenant, in a loud voice, explaining to the men outside the wood, that they were to suppose the bridge on the river below was held by the enemy. Now they were to march to the attack in such and such a manner. The lieutenant had no gift of expression. The orderly, listening from habit, got muddled. And when the lieutenant began it all again he ceased to hear.

He knew he must go. He stood up. It surprised him that the leaves were glittering in the sun, and the chips of wood reflecting white from the ground. For him a change had come over the world. But for the rest it had not—all seemed the same. Only he had left it. And he could not go back. It was his duty to return with the beer-pot and the bottle. He could not. He had left all that. The lieutenant was still hoarsely explaining. He must go, or they would overtake him. And he could not bear contact with anyone now.

He drew his fingers over his eyes, trying to find out where he was. Then he turned away. He saw the horse standing in the path. He went up to it and mounted. It hurt him to sit in the saddle. The pain of keeping his seat occupied him as they cantered through the wood. He would not have minded anything, but he could not get away from the sense of being divided from the others. The path led out of the trees. On the edge of the wood he pulled up and stood watching. There in the spacious sunshine of the valley soldiers were moving in a little swarm. Every now and then, a man harrowing on a strip of fallow shouted to his oxen, at the turn. The village and the white-towered church was small in the sunshine. And he no longer belonged to it—he sat there, beyond, like a man outside in the dark. He had gone out from everyday life into the unknown, and he could not, he even did not want to go back.

Turning from the sun-blazing valley, he rode deep into the wood. Tree-trunks, like people standing grey and still, took no notice as he went. A doe, herself a moving bit of sunshine and shadow, went running through the flecked shade. There were bright green rents in the foliage. Then it was all pine wood, dark and cool. And he was sick with pain, he had an intolerable great pulse in his head, and he was sick. He had never been ill in his life. He felt lost, quite dazed with all this.

Trying to get down from the horse, he fell, astonished at the pain and his lack of balance. The horse shifted uneasily. He jerked its bridle and sent it cantering jerkily away. It was his last connection with the rest of things.

But he only wanted to lie down and not be disturbed. Stumbling through the trees, he came on a quiet place where beeches and pine trees grew on a slope. Immediately he had lain down and closed his eyes, his consciousness went racing on without him. A big pulse of sickness beat in him as if it throbbed through the whole earth. He was burning with dry heat. But he was too busy, too tearingly active in the incoherent race of delirium to observe.

III

He came to with a start. His mouth was dry and hard, his heart beat heavily, but he had not the energy to get up. His heart beat heavily. Where was he?—the barracks—at home? There was something knocking. And, making an effort, he looked round—trees, and litter of greenery, and reddish, bright, still pieces of sunshine on the floor. He did not believe he was himself. He did not believe what he saw. Something was knocking. He made a struggle towards consciousness, but relapsed. Then he struggled again. And gradually his surroundings fell into relationship with himself. He knew, and a great pang of fear went through his heart. Somebody was knocking. He could see the heavy, black rags of a fir tree overhead. Then everything went black. Yet he did not believe he had closed his eyes. He had not. Out of the blackness sight slowly emerged again. And someone was knocking. Quickly, he saw the blood-disfigured face of his Captain, which he hated. And he held himself still with horror. Yet, deep inside him, he knew that it was so, the Captain should be dead. But the physical delirium got hold of him. Someone was knocking. He lay perfectly still, as if dead, with fear. And he went unconscious.

When he opened his eyes again, he started, seeing something creeping swiftly up a tree-trunk. It was a little bird. And the bird was whistling overhead. Tap-tap-tap—it was the small, quick bird rapping the tree-trunk with its beak, as if its head were a little round hammer. He watched it curiously. It shifted sharply, in its creeping fashion. Then, like a mouse, it slid down the bare trunk. Its swift creeping sent a flash of revulsion through him. He raised his head. It felt a great weight. Then, the little bird ran out of the shadow across a still patch of sunshine, its little head bobbing swiftly, its white legs twinkling brightly for a moment. How neat it was in its build, so compact, with pieces of white on its wings. There were several of them. They were so pretty—but they crept like swift, erratic mice, running here and there among the beech-mast.

He lay down again exhausted, and his consciousness lapsed. He had a horror of the little creeping birds. All his blood seemed to be darting and creeping in his head. And yet he could not move.

He came to with a further ache of exhaustion. There was the pain in his head, and the horrible sickness, and his inability to move. He had never been ill in his life. He did not know where he was or what he was. Probably he had got sunstroke. Or what else?—he had silenced the Captain for ever—some time ago—oh, a long time ago. There had been blood on his face, and his eyes had turned upwards. It was all right, somehow. It was peace. But now he had got beyond himself. He had never been here before. Was it life, or not life? He was by himself. They were in a big, bright place, those others, and he was outside. The town, all the country, a big bright place of light: and he was outside, here, in the darkened open beyond, where each thing existed alone. But they would all have to come out there sometime, those others. Little, and left behind him, they all were. There had been father and mother and sweetheart. What did they all matter? This was the open land.

He sat up. Something scuffled. It was a little brown squirrel running in lovely, undulating bounds over the floor, its red tail completing the undulation of its body—and then, as it sat up, furling and unfurling. He watched it, pleased. It ran on again, friskily, enjoying itself. It flew wildly at another squirrel, and they were chasing each other, and making little scolding, chattering noises. The soldier wanted to speak to them. But only a hoarse sound came out of his throat. The squirrels burst away—they flew up the trees. And then he saw the one peeping round at him, half-way up a tree-trunk. A start of fear went through him, though, in so far as he was conscious, he was amused. It still stayed, its little, keen face staring at him half-way up the tree-trunk, its little ears pricked up, its clawey little hands clinging to the bark, its white breast reared. He started from it in panic.

Struggling to his feet, he lurched away. He went on walking, walking, looking for something—for a drink. His brain felt hot and inflamed for want of water. He stumbled on. Then he did not know anything. He went unconscious as he walked. Yet he stumbled on, his mouth open.

When, to his dumb wonder, he opened his eyes on the world again, he no longer tried to remember what it was. There was thick, golden light behind golden-green glitterings, and tall, grey-purple shafts, and darknesses further off, surrounding him, growing deeper. He was conscious of a sense of arrival. He was amid the reality, on the real, dark bottom. But there was the thirst burning in his brain. He felt lighter, not so heavy. He supposed it was newness. The air was muttering with thunder. He thought he was walking wonderfully swiftly and was coming straight to relief—or was it to water?

Suddenly he stood still with fear. There was a tremendous flare of gold, immense—just a few dark trunks like bars between him and it. All the young level wheat was burnished gold glaring on its silky green. A woman, full-skirted, a black cloth on her head for headdress, was passing like a block of shadow through the glistening green corn, into the full glare. There was a farm, too, pale blue in shadow, and the timber black. And there was a church spire, nearly fused away in the gold. The woman moved on, away from him. He had no language with which to speak to her. She was the bright, solid unreality. She would make a noise of words that would confuse him, and her eyes would look at him without seeing him. She was crossing there to the other side. He stood against a tree.

When at last he turned, looking down the long, bare grove whose flat bed was already filling dark, he saw the mountains in a wonderlight, not far away, and radiant. Behind the soft, grey ridge of the nearest range the further mountains stood golden and pale grey, the snow all radiant like pure, soft gold. So still, gleaming in the sky, fashioned pure out of the ore of the sky, they shone in their silence. He stood and looked at them, his face illuminated. And like the golden, lustrous gleaming of the snow he felt his own thirst bright in him. He stood and gazed, leaning against a tree. And then everything slid away into space.

During the night the lightning fluttered perpetually, making the whole sky white. He must have walked again. The world hung livid round him for moments, fields a level sheen of grey-green light, trees in dark bulk, and the range of clouds black across a white sky. Then the darkness fell like a shutter, and the night was whole. A faint flutter of a half-revealed world, that could not quite leap out of the darkness!—

Then there again stood a sweep of pallor for the land, dark shapes looming, a range of clouds hanging overhead. The world was a ghostly shadow, thrown for a moment upon the pure darkness, which returned ever whole and complete.

And the mere delirium of sickness and fever went on inside him—his brain opening and shutting like the night—then sometimes convulsions of terror from something with great eyes that stared round a tree—then the long agony of the march, and the sun decomposing his blood—then the pang of hate for the Captain, followed by a pang of tenderness and ease. But everything was distorted, born of an ache and resolving into an ache.

In the morning he came definitely awake. Then his brain flamed with the sole horror of thirstiness! The sun was on his face, the dew was steaming from his wet clothes. Like one possessed, he got up. There, straight in front of him, blue and cool and tender, the mountains ranged across the pale edge of the morning sky. He wanted them—he wanted them alone—he wanted to leave himself and be identified with them. They did not move, they were still and soft, with white, gentle markings of snow. He stood still, mad with suffering, his hands crisping and clutching. Then he was twisting in a paroxysm on the grass.

He lay still, in a kind of dream of anguish. His thirst seemed to have separated itself from him, and to stand apart, a single demand. Then the pain he felt was another single self. Then there was the clog of his body, another separate thing. He was divided among all kinds of separate beings. There was some strange, agonized connection between them, but they were drawing further apart. Then they would all split. The sun, drilling down on him, was drilling through the bond. Then they would all fall, fall through the everlasting lapse of space. Then again, his consciousness reasserted itself. He roused on to his elbow and stared at the gleaming mountains. There they ranked, all still and wonderful between earth and heaven. He stared till his eyes went black, and the mountains, as they stood in their beauty, so clean and cool, seemed to have it, that which was lost in him.

IV

When the soldiers found him, three hours later, he was lying with his face over his arm, his black hair giving off heat under the sun. But he was still alive. Seeing the open, black mouth, the young soldiers dropped him in horror.

He died in the hospital at night, without having seen again.

The doctors saw the bruises on his legs, behind, and were silent.

The bodies of the two men lay together, side by side, in the mortuary, the one white and slender, but laid rigidly at rest, the other looking as if every moment it must rouse into life again, so young and unused, from a slumber.

STUDY QUESTIONS

1. What is the theme of this story?
2. Make a list of the characteristics of the two men. Can you generalize the essential conflict?
3. To what extent can one say that the characteristics of the two men are in reality the parts of a divided psyche? That both the officer and the soldier exist psychologically in all of us?
4. Do the characters seem to understand their motives?
5. What part could the officer's civilian experience have played in his motivation?
6. What reasons can you give for the causes of violence in this story? What seems to motivate the kicking scene?
7. Is there aesthetic or imaginative pleasure in one's reading of the violence and killing? Does it bring "relief" to the reader as it does to the soldier?
8. What do the mountains seem to mean to the soldier at the end?
9. What role does the imagery of nature and colors play in the meaning of the story? Note particularly the use of colors in the final paragraphs of the story.
10. What is the point of view in this story? Is it effective?

8

DRY SEPTEMBER*

William Faulkner

Born in New Albany, Mississippi, William Faulkner served in the British Royal Air Force in World War I. After the war he spent a brief time at the University of Mississippi and in Europe. He returned to Oxford, Mississippi where he began to create his mythological Yoknapatawpha County, a fictitious land which became the world of such novels as The Sound and the Fury *(1929),* As I Lay Dying *(1930),* Light in August *(1932),* Absalom, Absalom! *(1936), and* Go Down Moses *(1942). An early work,* Soldiers' Pay *(1926), and a late work,* A Fable *(1954), both concern World War I. In 1949 Faulkner was awarded the Nobel Prize for Literature. In this story Faulkner hints at disturbing causes at work in the vengeance and violence of a group of white men who punish a Negro for a "crime" against a white woman.*

I

THROUGH THE BLOODY September twilight, aftermath of sixty-two rainless days, it had gone like a fire in dry grass—the rumor, the story, whatever it was. Something about Miss Minnie Cooper and a Negro. Attacked, insulted, frightened: none of them, gathered in the barber shop on that Saturday evening where the ceiling fan stirred, without freshening it, the vitiated air, sending back upon them, in recurrent surges of stale pomade and lotion, their own stale breath and odors, knew exactly what had happened.

"Except it wasn't Will Mayes," a barber said. He was a man of middle age; a thin, sand-colored man with a mild face, who was shaving a client. "I know Will Mayes, He's a good nigger. And I know Miss Minnie Cooper, too."

"What do you know about her?" a second barber said.

"Who is she?" the client said. "A young girl?"

"No," the barber said. "She's about forty, I reckon. She aint married. That's why I dont believe—"

"Believe, hell!" a hulking youth in a sweat-stained silk shirt said. "Wont you take a white woman's word before a nigger's?"

"I dont believe Will Mayes did it," the barber said. "I know Will Mayes."

"Maybe you know who did it, then. Maybe you already got him out of town, you damn niggerlover."

"I dont believe anybody did anything. I dont believe anything happened. I leave it to you fellows if them ladies that get old without getting married dont have notions that a man cant—"

"Then you are a hell of a white man," the client said. He moved under the cloth. The youth had sprung to his feet.

"You dont?" he said. "Do you accuse a white woman of lying?"

The barber held the razor poised above the half-risen client. He did not look around.

"It's this durn weather," another said. "It's enough to make a man do anything. Even to her."

Nobody laughed. The barber said in his mild, stubborn tone. "I aint accusing nobody of nothing. I just know and you fellows know how a woman that never—"

"You damn niggerlover!" the youth said.

"Shut up, Butch," another said. "We'll get the facts in plenty of time to act."

"Who is? Who's getting them?" the youth said. "Facts, hell! I—"

"You're a fine white man," the client said. "Aint you?" In his frothy beard he looked like a desert rat in the moving pictures. "You tell them, Jack," he said to the youth. "If there aint any white men in this town, you can count on me, even if I aint only a drummer and a stranger."

"That's right, boys," the barber said. "Find out the truth first. I know Will Mayes."

"Well, by God!" the youth shouted. "To think that a white man in this town—"

"Shut up, Butch," the second speaker said. "We got plenty of time."

The client sat up. He looked at the speaker. "Do you claim that anything excuses a nigger attacking a white woman? Do you mean to tell me you are a white man and you'll stand for it? You better go back North where you came from. The South dont want your kind here."

"North what?" the second said. "I was born and raised in this town."

"Well, by God!" the youth said. He looked about with a strained, baffled gaze, as if he was trying to remember what it was he wanted to say or to do. He drew his sleeve across his sweating face. "Damn if I'm going to let a white woman—"

"You tell them, Jack," the drummer said. "By God, if they—"

The screen door crashed open. A man stood in the floor, his feet apart and his heavy-set body poised easily. His white shirt was open at the throat; he wore a felt hat. His hot, bold glance swept the group. His name was McLendon. He had commanded troops at the front in France and had been decorated for valor.

"Well," he said, "are you going to sit there and let a black son rape a white woman on the streets of Jefferson?"

Butch sprang up again. The silk of his shirt clung flat to his heavy shoulders. At each armpit was a dark halfmoon. "That's what I been telling them! That's what I—"

"Did it really happen?" a third said. "This aint the first man scare she ever had, like Hawkshaw says. Wasn't there something about a man on the kitchen roof, watching her undress, about a year ago?"

"What?" the client said. "What's that?" The barber had been slowly forcing him back into the chair; he arrested himself reclining, his head lifted, the barber still pressing him down.

McLendon whirled on the third speaker. "Happen? What the hell difference does it make? Are you going to let the black sons get away with it until one really does it?"

"That's what I'm telling them!" Butch shouted. He cursed, long and steady, pointless.

"Here, here," a fourth said; "Not so loud. Dont talk so loud."

"Sure," McLendon said; "no talking necessary at all. I've done my talking. Who's with me?" He poised on the balls of his feet, roving his gaze.

The barber held the drummer's face down, the razor poised. "Find out the facts first, boys. I know Willy Mayes. It wasn't him. Let's get the sheriff and do this thing right."

McLendon whirled upon him his furious, rigid face. The barber did not look away. They looked like men of different races. The other barbers had ceased also above their prone clients. "You mean to tell me," McLendon said, "that you'd take a nigger's word before a white woman's? Why, you damn niggerloving—"

The third speaker rose and grasped McLendon's arm; he too had been a soldier. "Now, now. Let's figure this thing out. Who knows anything about what really happened?"

"Figure out hell!" McLendon jerked his arm free. "All that're with me get up from there. The ones that aint—" He roved his gaze, dragging his sleeve across his face.

Three men rose. The drummer in the chair sat up. "Here," he said, jerking at the cloth about his neck; "get this rag off me. I'm with him. I dont live here, but by God, if our mothers and wives and sisters—" He smeared the cloth over his face and flung it to the floor. McLendon stood in the floor and cursed the others. Another rose and moved toward him. The remainder sat uncomfortable, not looking at one another, then one by one they rose and joined him.

The barber picked the cloth from the floor. He began to fold it neatly. "Boys, dont do that. Will Mayes never done it. I know."

"Come on," McLendon said. He whirled. From his hip pocket protruded the butt of a heavy automatic pistol. They went out. The screen door crashed behind them reverberant in the dead air.

The barber wiped the razor carefully and swiftly, and put it away, and ran to the rear, and took his hat from the wall. "I'll be back as soon as I can," he said to the other barbers. "I cant let—" He went out, running. The two other barbers followed him to the door and caught it on the rebound, leaning out and looking up the street after him. The air was flat and dead. It had a metallic taste at the base of the tongue.

"What can he do?" the first said. The second one was saying "Jees Christ, Jees Christ" under his breath. "I'd just as lief be Will Mayes as Hawk, if he gets McLendon riled."

"Jees Christ, Jees Christ," the second whispered.

"You reckon he really done it to her?" the first said.

2

She was thirty-eight or thirty-nine. She lived in a small frame house with her invalid mother and a thin, sallow, unflagging aunt, where each morning between ten and eleven she would appear on the porch in a lace-trimmed boudoir cap, to sit swinging in the porch swing until noon. After dinner she lay down for a while, until the afternoon began to cool. Then, in one of the three or four new voile dresses which she had each summer, she would go downtown to spend the afternoon in the stores with the other ladies, where they would handle the goods and haggle over the prices in cold, immediate voices, without any intention of buying.

She was of comfortable people—not the best in Jefferson, but good people enough—and she was still on the slender side of ordinary looking, with a bright, faintly haggard manner and dress. When she was young she had had a slender, nervous body and a sort of hard vivacity which had enabled her for a time to ride upon the crest of the town's social life as exemplified by the high school party and church social period of her contemporaries while still children enough to be unclass-conscious.

She was the last to realize that she was losing ground; that those among whom she had been a little brighter and louder flame than any other were beginning to learn the pleasure of snobbery—male—and retaliation—female. That was when her face began to wear that bright, haggard look. She still carried it to parties on shadowy porticos and summer lawns, like a mask or a flag with that bafflement and furious repudiation of truth in her eyes. One evening at a party she heard a boy and two girls, all schoolmates, talking. She never accepted another invitation.

She watched the girls with whom she had grown up as they married and got homes and children, but no man ever called on her steadily until the children of the other girls had been calling her "aunty" for several years, the while their mothers told them in bright voices about how popular Aunt Minnie had been as a girl. Then the town began to see her driving on Sunday afternoons with the cashier in the bank. He was a widower of about forty—a high-colored man, smelling always faintly of the barber shop or of whisky. He owned the first automobile in town, a red runabout; Minnie had the first motoring bonnet and veil the town ever saw. Then the town began to say: "Poor Minnie." "But she is old enough to take care of herself," others said. That was when she began to ask her old schoolmates that their children call her "cousin" instead of "aunty."

It was twelve years now since she had been relegated into adultery by public opinion, and eight years since the cashier had gone to a Memphis bank, returning for one day each Christmas, which he spent at an annual bachelors' party at a hunting club on the river. From behind their curtains the neighbors would see the party pass, and during the over-the-way Christmas day visiting they would tell her about him, about how well he looked, and how they heard that he was prospering in the city, watching with bright, secret eyes her haggard, bright face. Usually by that hour there would be the scent of whisky on her breath. It was supplied her by a youth, a clerk at the soda fountain: "Sure; I buy it for the old gal. I reckon she's entitled to a little fun."

Her mother kept to her room altogether now; the gaunt aunt ran the house. Against that background Minnie's bright dresses, her idle and empty days, had a quality of furious unreality. She went out in the evenings only with women now, neighbors, to the moving pictures. Each afternoon she dressed in one of the new dresses and went downtown alone, where her young "cousins" were already strolling in the late afternoons with their delicate, silken heads and thin, awkward arms and conscious hips, clinging to one another or shrieking and giggling with paired boys in the soda fountain when she passed and went on along the serried store fronts, in the doors of which the sitting and lounging men did not even follow her with their eyes any more.

3

The barber went swiftly up the street where the sparse lights, insect-swirled, glared in rigid and violent suspension in the lifeless air. The day had died in a pall of dust; above the darkened square, shrouded by the spent dust, the sky was as clear as the inside of a brass bell. Below the east was a rumor of the twice-waxed moon.

When he overtook them McLendon and three others were getting into a car parked in an alley. McLendon stooped his thick head, peering out beneath the top. "Changed your mind, did you?" he said. "Damn good thing; by God, tomorrow when this town hears about how you talked tonight—"

"Now, now," the other ex-soldier said. "Hawkshaw's all right. Come on, Hawk; jump in."

"Will Mayes never done it, boys," the barber said. "If anybody done it. Why, you all know well as I do there aint any town where they got better niggers than us. And you know how a lady will kind of think things about men when there aint any reason to, and Miss Minnie anyway—"

"Sure, sure," the soldier said. "We're just going to talk to him a little; that's all."

"Talk hell!" Butch said. "When we're through with the—"

"Shut up, for God's sake!" the soldier said. "Do you want everybody in town—"

"Tell them, by God!" McLendon said. "Tell every one of the sons that'll let a white woman—"

"Let's go; let's go: here's the other car." The second car slid squealing out of a cloud of dust at the alley mouth. McLendon started his car and took the lead. Dust lay like fog in the street. The street lights hung nimbused as in water. They drove on out of town.

A rutted land turned at right angles. Dust hung above it too, and above all the land. The dark bulk of the ice plant, where the Negro Mayes was night watchman, rose against the sky. "Better stop here, hadn't we?" the soldier said. McLendon did not reply. He hurled the car up and slammed to a stop, the headlights glaring on the blank wall.

"Listen here, boys," the barber said; "if he's here, dont that prove he never done it? Dont it? If it was him, he would run. Dont you see he would?" The second car came up and stopped. McLendon got down; Butch sprang down beside him. "Listen, boys," the barber said.

"Cut the lights off!" McLendon said. The breathless dark rushed down. There was no sound in it save their lungs as they sought air in the parched dust in which for two months they had lived; then the diminishing crunch of McLendon's and Butch's feet, and a moment later McLendon's voice:

"Will! . . . Will!"

Below the east the wan hemorrhage of the moon increased. It heaved above the ridge, silvering the air, the dust, so that they seemed to breathe, live, in a bowl of molten lead. There was no sound of nightbird nor insect, no sound save their breathing and a faint ticking of contracting metal about the cars. Where their bodies touched one another they seemed to sweat dryly, for no more moisture came. "Christ!" a voice said; "let's get out of here."

But they didn't move until vague noises began to grow out of the darkness ahead; then they got out and waited tensely in the breathless dark. There was another sound: a blow, a hissing expulsion of breath and McLendon cursing in undertone. They stood a moment longer, then they ran forward. They ran in a stumbling clump, as though they were fleeing something. "Kill him, kill the son," a voice whispered. McLendon flung them back.

"Not here," he said. "Get him into the car." "Kill him, kill the black son!" the voice murmured. They dragged the Negro to the car. The barber had waited beside the car. He could feel himself sweating and he knew he was going to be sick at the stomach.

"What is it, captains?" the Negro said, "I aint done nothing. 'Fore God, Mr John." Someone produced handcuffs. They worked busily about the Negro as though he were a post, quiet, intent, getting in one another's way. He submitted to the handcuffs, looking swiftly and constantly from dim face to dim face. "Who's here, captains?" he said, leaning to peer into the faces until they could feel his breath and smell his sweaty reek. He spoke a name or two. "What you all say I done, Mr John?"

McLendon jerked the car door open. "Get in!" he said.

The Negro did not move. "What you all going to do with me, Mr John? I aint done nothing. White folks, captains, I aint done nothing: I swear 'fore God." He called another name.

"Get in!" McLendon said. He struck the Negro. The others expelled their breath in a dry hissing and struck him with random blows and he whirled and cursed them, and swept his manacled hands across their faces and slashed the barber upon the mouth, and the barber struck him also. "Get him in there," McLendon said. They pushed at him. He ceased struggling and got in and sat quietly as the others took their places. He sat between the barber and the soldier, drawing his limbs in so as not to touch them, his eyes going swiftly and constantly from face to face. Butch clung to the running board. The car moved on. The barber nursed his mouth with his handkerchief.

"What's the matter, Hawk?" the soldier said.

"Nothing," the barber said. They regained the highroad and turned away from town. The second car dropped back out of the dust. They went on, gaining speed; the final fringe of houses dropped behind.

"Goddamn, he stinks!" the soldier said.

"We'll fix that," the drummer in front beside McLendon said. On the running board Butch cursed into the hot rush of air. The barber leaned suddenly forward and touched McLendon's arm.

"Let me out, John," he said.

"Jump out, niggerlover," McLendon said without turning his head. He drove swiftly. Behind them the sourceless lights of the second car glared in the dust. Presently McLendon turned into a narrow road. It was rutted with disuse. It led back to an abandoned brick kiln—a series of reddish mounds and weed- and vine-choked vats without bottom. It had been used for pasture once, until one day the owner missed one of his mules. Although he prodded carefully in the vats with a long pole, he could not even find the bottom of them.

"John," the barber said.

"Jump out, then," McLendon said, hurling the car along the ruts. Beside the barber the Negro spoke:

"Mr Henry."

The barber sat forward. The narrow tunnel of the road rushed up and past. Their motion was like an extinct furnace blast: cooler, but utterly dead. The car bounded from rut to rut.

"Mr Henry," the Negro said.

The barber began to tug furiously at the door. "Look out, there!" the soldier said, but the barber had already kicked the door open and swung onto the running board. The soldier leaned across the Negro and grasped at him, but he had already jumped. The car went on without checking speed.

The impetus hurled him crashing through dust-sheathed weeds, into the ditch. Dust puffed about him, and in a thin, vicious crackling of sapless stems he lay choking and retching until the second car passed and died away. Then he rose and limped on until he reached the highroad and turned toward town, brushing at his clothes with his hands. The moon was higher, riding high and clear of the dust at last, and after a while the town began to glare beneath the dust. He went on, limping. Presently he heard cars and the glow of them grew in the dust behind him and he left the road and crouched again in the weeds until they passed. McLendon's car came last now. There were four people in it and Butch was not on the running board.

They went on; the dust swallowed them; the glare and the sound died away. The dust of them hung for a while, but soon the eternal dust absorbed it again. The barber climbed back onto the road and limped on toward town.

4

As she dressed for supper on that Saturday evening, her own flesh felt like fever. Her hands trembled among the hooks and eyes, and her eyes had a feverish look, and her hair swirled crisp and crackling under the comb. While she was still dressing the friends called for her and sat while she donned her sheerest underthings and stockings and a new voile dress. "Do you feel strong enough to go out?" they said, their eyes bright too, with a dark glitter. "When you have had time to get over the shock, you must tell us what happened. What he said and did; everything."

In the leafed darkness, as they walked toward the square, she began to breathe deeply, something like a swimmer preparing to dive, until she ceased trembling, the four of them walking slowly because of the terrible heat and out of solicitude for her. But as they neared the square she began to tremble again, walking with her head up, her hands clenched at her sides, their voices about her murmurous, also with that feverish, glittering quality of their eyes.

They entered the square, she in the center of the group, fragile in her fresh dress. She was trembling worse. She walked slower and slower, as children eat ice cream, her head up and her eyes bright in the haggard banner of her face, passing the hotel and the coatless drummers in chairs along the curb looking around at her: "That's the one: see? The one in pink in the middle." "Is that her? What did they do with the nigger? Did they—?" "Sure. He's all right." "All right, is he?" "Sure. He went on a little trip." Then the drug store, where even the young men lounging in the doorway tipped their hats and followed with their eyes the motion of her hips and legs when she passed.

They went on, passing the lifted hats of the gentlemen, the suddenly ceased voices, deferent, protective. "Do you see?" the friends said. Their voices sounded like long, hovering sighs of hissing exultation. "There's not a Negro on the square. Not one."

They reached the picture show. It was like a miniature fairyland with its lighted lobby and colored lithographs of life caught in its terrible and beautiful mutations. Her lips began to tingle. In the dark, when the picture began, it would be all right; she could hold back the laughing so it would not waste away so fast and so soon. So she hurried on before the turning faces, the undertones of low astonishment, and they took their accustomed places where she could see the aisle against the silver and glare and the young men and girls coming in two and two against it.

The lights flicked away; the screen glowed silver, and soon life began to unfold, beautiful and passionate and sad, while still the young men and girls entered, scented and sibilant in the half dark, their paired backs in silhouette delicate and sleek, their slim, quick bodies awkward, divinely young, while beyond them the silver dream accumulated, inevitably on and on. She began to laugh. In trying to suppress it, it made more noise than ever; heads began to turn. Still laughing, her friends raised her and led her out, and she stood at the curb, laughing on a high, sustained note, until the taxi came up and they helped her in.

They removed the pink voile and the sheer underthings and the stockings, and put her to bed, and cracked ice for her temples, and sent for the doctor. He was hard to locate, so they ministered to her with hushed ejaculations, renewing the ice and fanning her. While the ice was fresh and cold she stopped laughing and lay still for a time, moaning only a little. But soon the laughing welled again and her voice rose screaming.

Shhhhhhhhhhh! Shhhhhhhhhhhhh!" they said, freshening the icepack, smoothing her hair, examining it for gray; "poor girl!" Then to one another: "Do you suppose anything really happened?" their eyes darkly aglitter, secret and passionate. "Shhhhhhhhhh! Poor girl! Poor Minnie!"

5

It was midnight when McLendon drove up to his neat new house. It was trim and fresh as a birdcage and almost as small, with its clean, green-and-white paint. He locked the car and mounted the porch and entered. His wife rose from a chair beside the reading lamp. McLendon stopped in the floor and stared at her until she looked down.

"Look at that clock," he said, lifting his arm, pointing. She stood before him, her face lowered, a magazine in her hands. Her face was pale, strained, and weary-looking. "Haven't I told you about sitting up like this, waiting to see when I come in?"

"John," she said. She laid the magazine down. Poised on the balls of his feet, he glared at her with his hot eyes, his sweating face.

"Didn't I tell you?" He went toward her. She looked up then. He caught her shoulder. She stood passive, looking at him.

"Don't, John. I couldn't sleep . . . The heat; something. Please, John. You're hurting me."

"Didn't I tell you?" He released her and half struck, half flung her across the chair, and she lay there and watched him quietly as he left the room.

He went on through the house, ripping off his shirt, and on the dark, screened porch at the rear he stood and mopped his head and shoulders with the shirt and flung it away. He took the pistol from his hip and laid it on the table beside the bed, and sat on the bed and removed his shoes, and rose and slipped his trousers off. He was sweating again already, and he stooped and hunted furiously for the shirt. At last he found it and wiped his body again, and, with his body pressed against the dusty screen, he stood panting. There was no movement, no sound, not even an insect. The dark world seemed to lie stricken beneath the cold moon and the lidless stars.

STUDY QUESTIONS

1. What is the symbolic meaning of the title?
2. What are the motives for violence in this story? Support your view with evidence.
3. How would you describe the behavior of the men in the barber-shop? What reasons would you give for their behavior?
4. Why does the barber strike Will Mayes?
5. Why does McLendon strike his wife?
6. How does the first paragraph foreshadow the violence that is to come?
7. How is Miss Minnie characterized? Explain her hysteria.
8. Is there a sense of guilt in this story? To what extent does guilt contribute to violence?

9

PRISHCHEPA*

Isaac Babel

Born in Odessa, Russia, Isaac Babel was a famous Russian short story writer and dramatist. He won immediate fame for the Russian-Jewish stories of his Odessa Tales *(1923-1924) and for his stories of Cossacks in* Red Cavalry *(1926). Later he turned to drama with* Sunset *(1928) and* Maria *(1935). He was arrested in 1938 following criticism of his work by the Communist Party. After the death of Stalin, some of Babel's works were republished in the Soviet Union. In this brief story Babel reveals to us the ambiguities of vengeance as a returning Cossack reclaims what once belonged to his family.*

I AM APPROACHING Leszniow where division headquarters is now. Once again, my traveling companion is Prishchepa, a young Kuban Cossack, an inveterate bully who has been expelled from the Communist Party, a future junkman, a lighthearted syphilitic, an unhurried liar. He wears a raspberry-colored Circassian jacket of fine cloth with a quilted hood hanging down his back.

A year earlier, Prishchepa had come over to our side from the Whites. They avenged themselves by arresting his parents and killing them. Everything belonging to them was grabbed by their neighbors. When the Kuban was cleared of the Whites, Prishchepa returned to his native village.

It was morning, dawn, the peasants' sleep was sighing in acrid stuffiness. Prishchepa got hold of an official wagon and drove all over the village, collecting his phonograph, his cider jugs, and the tablecloths his mother had embroidered.

He walked along the street in a black fur cloak with a dagger stuck in his belt. The wagon plodded behind him. Prishchepa went from

---

*From **LYUBKA THE COSSACK** by Isaac Babel, translated by Andrew R. MacAndrew, copyright © 1963 by Andrew MacAndrew. Reprinted by arrangement with The New American Library, Inc., New York.

house to house, his boots leaving a gory trail behind him. In huts where he found his mother's handiwork or his father's pipes, he would leave an old woman stabbed, a dog hanged over a well, an icon filthied with dung.

The old Cossack villagers watched him sullenly, smoking their pipes. The young men scattered in the steppe and kept the score. It kept swelling, but the village was silent.

When he was through, Prishchepa returned to his father's house. He put the recovered objects back in their old places, as he remembered them from his childhood. Then he sent for vodka, locked himself in and, for two days, drank, sang, cried, and chopped at the furniture with his sword.

On the third night, the villagers saw smoke rising above Prishchepa's hut. Scorched and drunk, he emerged from the hut, went to the barn, took out his cow, placed his gun in her mouth, and fired. The ground smoked under him, a blue ring of flame escaped from the chimney and melted, an abandoned bull calf bellowed piteously in the barn. The fire gleamed like a Sunday.

Prishchepa then untied his horse and jumped into the saddle; he yanked a tuft of hair out of his head, threw it into the fire, and rode off, soon vanishing from sight.

STUDY QUESTIONS

1. In what period of history is this story set? What significant event had just occurred? Who were the Whites and who were their victorious opponents?

2. What form of revenge did Prishchepa inflict on those villagers who had taken his parents' possessions? What does this suggest to you about the value placed by this society on the life of an elderly person?

3. Why didn't the young men of the village counter Prishchepa's violence with violence of their own?

4. Did Prishchepa really want his parents' stolen possessions? What do you think was his reasoning in first reclaiming, then destroying them? Why did he throw a tuft of his own hair in the fire as he left?

5. What picture of the quality of life people led during this period in history does this story bring to mind in you?

10

From THE NAKED AND THE DEAD*

Norman Mailer

Born in Long Branch, New Jersey, Norman Mailer was graduated from Harvard in 1943, and served with the army during World War II. His novel The Naked and the Dead *(1948) established him immediately as a significant figure in American writing. Since then he has given us such works as* The Deer Park *(1955),* An American Dream *(1965),* Why Are We in Vietnam? *(1967). In addition, he has published significant collections of shorter pieces,* Advertisements For Myself *(1959) and* The Presidential Papers *(1963). Most recently his works include* The Armies of the Night *(1968) and* Of a Fire on the Moon *(1970).*

In The Naked and the Dead, *Mailer gives us a wide panorama of fighting men in the Pacific during World War II. Though the story is set on Anopopei, a Pacific island, Mailer manages to give us a complex and wide range of characters, actions, politics, and philosophies in conflict. Through the device of the "Time Machine" Mailer reveals how his characters have developed from the realities of American society before the war. This device gives us the deeper dimensions and motivations of the characters. In the first of the following excerpts we see Sgt. Croft in action. In the "Time Machine" we are given some reasons for Sgt. Croft's long list of brutalities in the organized violence of war.*

THE PRISONER shook his head slowly, and smiled again.

Croft came up to him, and gave him another cigarette. The Japanese soldier bowed low, and accepted the match. "Arigato, arigato, domo arigato," he said.

Croft felt his head pulsing with an intense excitement. There were tears in the prisoner's eyes again, and Croft looked at them dispassion-

---

*From **THE NAKED AND THE DEAD** by Norman Mailer. Reprinted by permission of the author and the author's agents, Scott Meredith Literary Agency, Inc.

ately. He gazed once about the little draw, and watched a fly crawl over the mouth of one of the corpses.

The prisoner had taken a deep puff and was leaning back now against the trunk of the tree. His eyes had closed, and for the first time there was a dreamy expression on his face. Croft felt a tension work itself into his throat and leave his mouth dry and bitter and demanding. His mind had been entirely empty until now, but abruptly he brought up his rifle and pointed it at the prisoner's head. Gallagher started to protest as the Jap opened his eyes.

The prisoner did not have time to change his expression before the shot crashed into his skull. He slumped forward, and then rolled on his side. He was still smiling but he looked silly now.

the time machine:

SAM CROFT

THE HUNTER

A lean man of medium height but he held himself so erectly he appeared tall. His narrow triangular face was utterly without expression. There seemed nothing wasted in his hard small jaw, gaunt firm cheeks and straight short nose. His gelid eyes were very blue . . . he was efficient and strong and usually empty and his main cast of mind was a superior contempt toward nearly all other men. He hated weakness and he loved practically nothing. There was a crude unformed vision in his soul but he was rarely conscious of it.

NO, BUT WHY *is* Croft that way?

Oh, there are answers. He is that way because of the corruption-of-the-society. He is that way because the devil has claimed him for one of his own. It is because he is a Texan; it is because he has renounced God.

He is that kind of man, because the only woman he ever loved cheated on him, or he was born that way, or he was having problems of adjustment.

Croft's father, Jesse Croft, liked to say, "Well, now, my Sam is a mean boy. I reckon he was whelped mean." And then Jesse Croft, thinking of his wife who was ailing, a weak woman sweet and mild, might add, " 'Course Sam got mother's milk if ever a one did, but Ah figger it turned sour for him 'cause that was the only way his stomach would take it." Then he would cackle and blow his nose into his hand and wipe it on the back of his pale-blue dungarees. (Standing before his dirty wood barn, the red dry soil of western Texas under his feet.) "Why, Ah 'member once Ah took Sam huntin', he was only an itty-bitty runt, not big enough to hold up the gun hardly . . . but he was a mean shot from the beginning. And Ah'll tell ya, he just didn't like to have a man interfere with him. That was one thing could always rile him, even when he was an itty-bitty bastard.

"Couldn't stand to have anyone beat him in anythin'.

"Never could lick him. Ah'd beat the piss out o' him, and he'd never make a sound. Jus' stand there lookin' at me as if he was fixin' to wallop me back, or maybe put a bullet in mah head."

Croft hunted early. In the winter, in the chill Texas desert, it used to be a cold numbing ride across twenty miles of rutted hard-baked road with the dust blowing like emery into the open battered Ford. The two big men in the front would say little, and the one who was not driving would blow on his fingers. When they reached the forest, the sun would still be straining to rise above the brown-red line of ridge.

Now, look, boy, see that trail, that's a deer run. They ain't hardly a man is smart enough to track down a deer. You set an' wait for 'em, and you set where the wind is blowin' down from the deer to you. You got to wait a long time.

The boy sits shivering in the wood. Ah'm fugged if Ah'll wait for any ole deer. Ah'm gonna track 'em.

He stalks through the forest with the wind on his face. It's dark, and the trees are silver-brown, and the ground is a deep-olive velvet. Where is that ole deer? He kicks a twig out of his way, and stiffens as a buck goes clattering through the brush. Goddam! Ole deer is fast.

Next time he is more cautious. He finds a deer track, kneels down and traces the hoofprint tenderly, feeling a thrill. Ah'm gonna track this old deer.

For two hours he creeps through the forest, watching where he places his feet, putting his heel down first, then his toes before he shifts his weight. When the dried thorny branches catch in his clothing, he pulls them free quietly, one by one.

In a little clearing he sees a deer and freezes. The wind is blowing gently against his face, and he thinks he can smell the animal. Goddam, he whispers to himself. What a big ole bastard. The stag turns slowly, looks past him from a hundred yards. Sonofabitch cain't see me.

The boy raises his gun, and trembles so badly the sights waver. He lowers it, and curses himself. Jus' a little ole woman. He brings it up again, holding it steadily, moving the front sight over until it points a few inches below the muscle of the foreleg. Ah'm goin' to git him through the heart.

BAA-WOWW!

It is someone else's gun, and the deer drops. The boy runs forward almost weeping. Who shot him? That was mah deer. I'll kill the sonofabitch who shot him.

Jesse Croft is laughing at him. Ah tole you, boy, to set where Ah put you.

Ah tracked that deer.

You scared that deer into me. Ah heard ya footing it from a mile away.

You're a liar. You're a goddam liar. The boy throws himself at his father, and tries to strike him.

Jesse Croft gives him a blow across the mouth, and he sits down. You ole sonofabitch, he screams, and flings himself at his father again.

Jesse holds him off, laughing. Little ole wildcat, ain't ya? Well, you got to wait ten years 'fore you can whop your pa.

That deer was mine.

One that wins is the one that gits it.

The tears freeze in the boy's eyes and wither. He is thinking that if he hadn't trembled he would have shot the deer first.

"Yes, sir," Jesse Croft said, "they wa'n' a thing my Sam could stand to have ya beat him in. When he was 'bout twelve, they was a fool kid down at Harper who used to give Sam a lickin'." (Scratching the back of his gray scraggly hair, his hat in his hand.) "That kid would lick Sam every day, and Sam would go back and pick a fight the next day. Ah'll tell ya, he ended up by whoppin' the piss out of that kid.

"And then when he was older, about seventeen maybe, he used to be bustin' horses down to the fair in August, and he was known to be 'bout the best rider in the country. Then one time a fella all the way from Denison came down and beat him in a reg'lar competition with judges and all. I 'member Sam was so mad he wouldn't talk to no one for two days.

"He got good stock in him," Jesse Croft declared to his neighbors. "We was one of the first folks to push in here, must be sixty years ago, and they was Crofts in Texas over a hunnerd years ago. Ah'd guess some of them had that same meanness that Sam's got. Maybe it was what made 'em push down here."

Deer hunting and fighting and busting horses at the fair make up in hours a total of perhaps ten days a year. There are the other things, the long flat sweeps of the terrain, the hills in the distance, the endless meals in the big kitchen with his parents and brothers and the ranch foreman.

There are the conversations in the bunkhouse. The soft reflective voices.

Ah tell ya that little gal is gonna remember me unless she was too goddam drunk.

Ah jus' looked at that nigger after that, an' Ah said, Boy, you no-good black bastard, an' Ah jus' picked up that hatchet an' let him have it right across the head. But the sonofabitch didn't even bleed much. You can kill an elephant about as fast as you can kill a nigger in the head.

A whoor is no damn good for a man, Ah gotta have it at least five six times 'fore Ah'm satisfied, and that ole business of stickin' it in once an' then reachin' for your hat jus' leaves me more fussed than it's worth.

Ah been keepin' an eye on that south herd leader, the red one with the spot 'hind his ear, an' he's gonna be gittin' mean when the hot weather comes.

The Education of Samuel Croft.

And always, day after day, the dust of cattle through the long shimmering afternoons in the sun. A man gets bored and it's uncomfortable falling asleep in a saddle. Thinking of town maybe. (Bar and a whorehouse, dry goods.)

Sam, you gittin' itchy?

A lazy somnolent pulsing in his loins. The sun refracts from the hide of his horse, bathes his thighs in a lazy heat. Yeah, some.

They're fixin' to start a National Guard outfit in Harper.

Yeah?

Ah figger they'll be some women hangin' round the uniforms, an' ya git to do a lot of shootin'.

Maybe I'll go down with ya. He wheels his horse to the left and rides out to turn back a straggler.

The first time Croft ever killed a man he was in a National Guard uniform. There was a strike on at Lilliput in the oil fields, and some scabs had been hurt.

They called the Guard. (The sonsofbitches started this strike come from up north, New York. They's some good boys in the oil fields but they got they heads turned by Reds, an' next thing they'll have ya kissin' niggers' asses.) The guardsmen made a line against the gate to the plant and stood sweating in a muggy summer sun. The pickets yelled and jeered at them.

Hey, drillers, they called out the Boy Scouts.

Let's rush 'em. They're jus' company scabs too.

Croft stands in line with his mouth tightening.

They're gonna rush us, the soldier next to him says.

The Guard lieutenant is a haberdashery salesman. If there're rocks being thrown you better lie down, men. If it should git real bad, fire a couple of rounds over their heads.

A stone lofts through the air. The crowd is sullen outside the gate, and every now and then one of them shouts some curses at the soldiers.

No sonofabitch'll talk to me that way, Croft says.

A rock strikes one of the soldiers, and they lie down on the ground and point their rifles above the heads of the advancing crowd.

Let's rip the place apart.

About ten men start to walk toward the gate. Some stones fly over their heads and scatter among the soldiers.

All right, men, the lieutenant pipes, fire over them.

Croft sights down his barrel. He has pointed his gun at the chest of the nearest man, and he feels a curious temptation.

I'll just squeeze the trigger a little bit.

BAA-WOWWW! The shot is lost in the volley, but the striker drops.

Croft feels a hollow excitement.

The lieutenant is cursing. Goddam, who shot him, men?

Guess they's no way to find out, Lieutenant, Croft says. He watches the mob retreating in a panic. Bunch o' dogs, he tells himself. His heart is beating, and his hands feel very dry.

" 'Member that gal, Janey, he married. Ah'll say one thing for her, she was a reg'lar ole tomcat," Jesse Croft said. (He spewed an oyster of phlegm, and ground it reflectively with his boot.) "Jus' the meanest little ole girl, Ah'll tell ya she was a mate for him till they busted up. They ain't one of the gals my boys've married that I woulda taken up against her. Ah'm an old man, but Ah'll tell ya, mah balls would git to itchin' when Ah'd look at her and jus' think of lovin' up to her." (Scratching his pants vigorously.) "Trouble with Sam he shouldn'ta married her. When a man can knock off a piece with a woman without slippin' her a weddin' ring, it don' pay to git any ideas about settlin' down with her. A woman that likes her nookie ain't gonna be satisfied with one man after she gits used to him." (Pointing his finger at the man he is talking to.) "Reckon that's a law of life."

Oh, give it to me, you sonofabitch, give it to me, I'LL KILL YOU IF YOU STOP.

Who's your man?

You're my man, you give it to me, give it to me, give it to me.

They ain't nobody can make love to you like me.

They ain't anybody, anybody, oh, you're just a goddam fuggin machine.

The long sliding of a belly against a belly.

I love ya better than any man ever could.

You do, baby, you do.

Ah'm jus' an old fuggin machine. (Crack . . . that . . . whip! Crack . . . that . . . WHIP!)

After they married, Croft rented a little house on the ranch from his father. He and Janey petered out for each other through a slow taciturn year, through a thousand incidents which they forgot while the effects still remained. At night they would sit by themselves in the parlor, listen to the radio and seldom talk. In a dumb instinctive way, Croft would search for an approach.

Want to go to bed?

It's early, Sam.

Yeah. And an anger would work in him. They had torn at each other once, had felt sick when they were close together and other people were with them. Now, in sleep their bodies intruded; there was always a heavy limb in the way. And the nights together working on them, this new change, this living together between them like a heavy dull weight, washing dishes and mouthing familiar kisses.

The buddy-system.

But he wanted no buddy. In the quiet nights in the cheap parlor of this house set on the Texas plains, an undefined rage increased and increased. There were the things he did not know how to utter (the great space of the night), the fury between them balked almost completely now. There were the trips to town, the drinking bouts between them, the occasional kindling of their bodies in a facsimile of their earlier passion, only confusing and protracting the irreversible reaction.

It ended with him going to town alone, and taking a whore when he was drunk, beating her sometimes with a wordless choler. And for Janey it resulted in other men, ranch hands, once one of his brothers.

"It jus' don' pay to marry a woman with hot pants," Jesse Croft said later.

Croft found out in a quarrel.

And another thing, you go tomcattin' to town, and jus' hellin' around, well, don' be thinkin' Ah'm jus' sittin' around. They's things Ah can tell you too.

What things?

You want to know, don't ya? You got yore water hot. Jus' don' push me around.

What things?

She laughs. Jus' a way of talkin'.

Croft slaps her across the face, catches her wrists and shakes her.

WHAT THINGS?

You sonofabitch. (Her eyes glaring.) You know what kind of things. He strikes her so heavily that she falls.

That's one thing you ain't best in, she screams.

Croft stands there trembling and then wrenches out of the room. (Goddam whore.) He feels nothing and then anger and shame and then nothing again. At this moment his initial love, his initial need of her is full-throated again. (Jus' an ole fuggin machine.)

"If Sam coulda found any of the boys who was scooting up her pants, he'da killed 'em," Jesse Croft said. "He tore around like he was gonna choke us all with his hands and then he took off for town and threw himself about as good a drunk as Ah've seen him indulge. And when he got back he'd enlisted himself in the Army."

After that there were always other men's wives.

You must think I'm a pretty cheap woman going out with you like this.

Wouldn't say that. Everybody likes to have a good time.

That's it. (Drinking her beer.) That's my philosophy. Need to have a good time. You don't think a bit cheap of me, do you, soldier?

Hell, you're too good-lookin' a woman for me to think cheap. (Have another beer.)

And later. Jack don't treat me right. You understand me.

That's right, honey, I understand you. They roll together in bed.

Ain't nothing wrong with that philosophy, she says.

Not a damn thing wrong. (And . . . crack . . . that . . . WHIP!)

You're all fuggin whores, he thinks.

His ancestors pushed and labored and strained, drove their oxen, sweated their women, and moved a thousand miles.

He pushed and labored inside himself and smoldered with an endless hatred.

(You're all a bunch of fuggin whores)

(You're all a bunch of dogs)

(You're all deer to track)

I HATE EVERYTHING WHICH IS NOT IN MYSELF

STUDY QUESTIONS

1. Why does Mailer call this section of his novel, "The Hunter"? Can you think of another title that would be equally appropriate?
2. Reconstruct Croft's family life. What effect does it have upon his ways of thinking and acting?
3. A number of reasons are given at the beginning to explain why Croft is the way he is. Which reason do you think is most likely to produce a man like Croft? What seems to be the chief motivation for Croft's killing of the striker?
4. What is the nature of Croft's relationship with his wife? Is there any evidence of love in their relationship? Is there a relationship between sex and violence?
5. Is Croft a believable character? Is the killing of the prisoner a believable act in the light of Croft's background? Why?
6. Mailer shows a necessary connection between a man's behavior and the values of his culture. If a man is a product of his culture, to what extent can we hold him responsible for his behavior, especially under the pressures of war? Can a man be in conflict with his culture? If so, on what grounds can he justify his own values and actions?
7. Is the killing of prisoners in war ever justified? What are the values that could lead one to the killing of prisoners? Of enemy civilians? Create an imaginative situation in which the killing of prisoners or civilians would be justified.
8. Drawing upon your experience and knowledge of American values, would you say that Croft could be representative of a significant number of Americans?

11

CRIME AT THE TENNIS CLUB*

Alberto Moravia

Born in Rome, Alberto Moravia has become, since World War II, a leading Italian writer of wide international appeal. His first novel, Gli Indifferenti, was completed in 1927 when he was 20 years old and two years later Moravia found himself a literary celebrity. In his novels, he repeatedly returns to Italian bourgeois society as he anatomizes the neuroses of modern man. Among his works are The Woman of Rome (1949), The Empty Canvas (1961), and Two Women (1958).

In this story by Moravia, the young men of respectable background begin by playing a joke on a middle-aged "Princess." Before long they are nightmarishly involved in an act of violence. The result: something no one had expected.

ABOUT THE MIDDLE of the winter the Committee of one of the best-known tennis clubs in our town decided to give a grand Gala Ball. The Committee, which consisted of Messrs. Lucini, Mastrogiovanni, Costa, Ripandelli and Micheli, set aside a certain sum of money for providing champagne and other drinks and refreshments, and for the hire of a good band, and then went on to draw up a list of those who should be invited. The members of the club belonged for the most part to the class which is commonly called the upper middle class; they were all of them the offspring of rich and respected families and—since one has to have a job of some kind—they all carried on the appearance, anyhow, of some profession or other: and so it was not difficult to assemble, from amongst relations, friends and acquaintances, an adequate number of names, many of which were preceded by titles of nobility of secondary importance but none the less decorative that would later give an aristocratic lustre to the event in the society columns of the newspapers. At the last moment, however, when there was nothing left to be done but send out the invitations, there suddenly arose—as generally happens—an unforeseen difficulty.

"How about the 'Princess'—aren't we going to invite her?" asked Ripandelli, a young man of about thirty, handsome in a somewhat Southern style, with glossy black hair, black eyes, and a dark, oval face with perfect features; he was known for his resemblance to one of the most celebrated of American film stars and was quite aware of this and made use of it to make an impression upon women.

Mastrogiovanni, Lucini and Micheli approved the idea of inviting the "Princess"; she would provide an extra bit of fun, they said, possibly the only bit of fun; and with loud bursts of laughter and mutual back-slappings they reminded one another of what had happened last time: how the "Princess" had had so much champagne that she was quite drunk, and someone had hidden her shoes, and she had been forced to wait until the last guests had left so that she could walk out in her stockinged feet . . . .

It was only Costa—bird of ill omen, as they called him—the tall, ungainly Costa, with big tortoiseshell-rimmed spectacles on his long nose and his thin cheeks never properly shaved—it was only Costa who protested.

"No," he said; "let her stay at home this, time, the Princess . . . I had quite enough of her at the last dance. If you want some fun you can go and pay her a visit, but don't do it here . . . ."

His companions rebelled and told him exactly what they thought of him—that he was a spoil-sport and a fool and that, in any case, he didn't own the club.

They had been sitting for two hours in the little committee-room and the air was thick with cigarette-smoke; it was warm and damp in the room on account of the fresh plaster of the walls, and they were all wearing thick sweaters of various colours under their coats. But outside, projecting across the panes of the window, could be seen a single fir branch, so still, so melancholy against the grey background of the sky that there was no need to go over and look out in order to see whether it was raining. Costa rose to his feet.

"I know," he spoke emphatically, "I know your intention is to play some kind of dirty trick on that unfortunate woman. . . . Well, I tell you once and for all—you're mean cads and you ought to be ashamed of yourselves."

"Costa, I thought you were more intelligent," Ripandelli declared, without moving from his place.

"And I didn't think you were so evil-minded," replied Costa; he took down his overcoat from its hook and went out without saying good-bye. After five minutes' discussion, the Committee decided unanimously to invite the Princess to the ball.

* * *

The ball began a little after ten o'clock in the evening. It had been raining all day and it was a damp, misty night; down at the far end of the suburban avenue in which the club-house stood could be seen, in the dim distance between two dark rows of plane-trees, a glow and a confused movement of lights and vehicles as the guests arrived. In the vestibule a hired man-servant relieved them of their coats and wraps, and then the women in their light evening dresses, the men in tail coats, all moved on, talking and laughing, into the large, brilliantly-lit ball-room.

This room was of considerable size and reached up to the full height of the building: a gallery with a blue-painted wooden balustrade ran around it at first-floor level, and out of this gallery opened a few small rooms which were used as dressing-rooms and for the storage of games equipment. An enormous chandelier in the same style and of the same colour as the balustrade hung from the ceiling, and attached to it, for the occasion, were festoons of Venetian lanterns stretching away to the four corners of the room; the wainscot was also painted blue; and at the far end, fitted in underneath the corner of the little staircase leading to the floor above was the refreshment bar, with its bright-coloured rows of bottles and its shining coffee-machine.

The "Princess", who was not a princess at all but, so it was said, merely a countess (it was also rumoured that once upon a time she had moved in high society and had been banished from it because of some ugly story of adultery, elopement and financial ruin), arrived soon after eleven o'clock. Ripandelli, who was sitting with a group of ladies opposite the wide-open door into the vestibule, saw the well-known figure—short, rather squat, with feet turned outwards like a web-footed bird—as, with her slightly bent back turned towards him, she handed her cloak to the manservant. "There we are," he thought, and, his heart filled with exultation, he went across through the dancing throng to meet her, reaching her just in time to stop her slapping the face of the manservant, with whom, for some futile reason of her own, she had picked a quarrel.

"Welcome, welcome!" he called to her from the doorway.

"Ah, Ripandelli, come and deliver me from this brute!" she said as she turned towards him. The Princess's face was not beautiful. From beneath a forest of curly hair, cut very short, her black eyes, round and beset with wrinkles, shone out livid and wild-looking; the nostrils of her long, sensual nose were full of hairs; her wide mouth, its lips painted and age-roughened, was unceasingly lavish of brilliant, fatuous, conventional smiles. The Princess dressed in a manner that was at the same showy and shabby: over her out-of-date dress, with its long skirt and a bodice so tight that the two long, meagre swellings of her bosom caught the light, she had thrown a black shawl embroidered with birds, flowers and arabesques of every possible colour—in order, perhaps, to conceal an excessively low neckline; and across her forehead she had tied a band, from beneath which her rebellious hair escaped in all directions. Thus adorned, and laden with artificial jewels, she made her entrance into the ballroom, peering ahead through a silver-rimmed eyeglass.

Luckily, the turmoil of dancing couples prevented her being noticed. Ripandelli steered her into a corner. "Dear Princess," he said, at once assuming an impudent tone of voice, "whatever would have happened to us if you hadn't come?"

The deluded expression in her eyes showed clearly that she took quite seriously any stupid thing that was said to her; but out of coquettishness she replied: "You young men try to hook all the women you can . . . and the more you catch, the better for you. Isn't that so?"

"Shall we dance, Princess?" asked Ripandelli, rising. He led her on to the floor. "You dance like a feather," said the young man, as he felt the full weight of her body pressing heavily on his arm.

"Everyone tells me that," answered the shrill voice. Crushed against Ripandelli's starched shirt-front the Princess, palpitating, seemed in a ravishment of ecstasy. Ripandelli became bolder. "Well, Princess, when are you going to invite me to your house?"

"I have a very small circle of friends," replied the unfortunate woman, who notoriously, lived in complete solitude; "only the other day I was saying the same thing to the Duke of L., who was asking the same favour of me . . . a very limited circle of carefully selected people. One can't be too careful nowadays, you know."

"Ugly old bitch," thought Ripandelli. "No, no," he went on, aloud, "I don't want to be invited with everybody else. You must let me come and see you in an intimate sort of way . . . in your own boudoir, for instance . . . or perhaps . . . or perhaps in your bedroom."

This was an audacity, but she accepted it without protest. "And if I invite you," she asked, in a voice that was tender and a little breathless owing to the emotion of the dance, "will you promise me to be good?"

"As good as gold."

"Then I'll allow you to take me home this evening . . . . You have a car, haven't you?"

The dance was finished now and, as the crowd passed slowly into the refreshment room, Ripandelli mentioned a little private room on the first floor, where a bottle of champagne awaited them. "This way," he said, indicating the staircase; "up here we shall be able to talk more intimately."

"Oh, you're a rascal, you are," she said, hurrying up the stairs and threatening him with her eyeglass; "you think of everything."

The little private room was a small place with rows of white lockers round the walls, in which racquets and tennis-balls were usually kept. In the middle, on a table, was a bottle of champagne in an ice-bucket. The young man closed the door, invited the Princess to sit down, and immediately poured her out a drink.

"To the health of the most beautiful of princesses"—he stood facing her as he gave the toast—"and the woman I think about night and day!"

"Here's to your health too!" she replied, bewildered and excited. She had dropped her shawl now, and her shoulders and bosom were displayed. The thin back might have been that of a woman still young, but in front, where the edge of her dress slipped downwards with every movement, first on one side and then on the other, the discoloration of the yellowing, wrinkled flesh revealed the ravages of advancing age. Ripandelli, his head resting on his hand, was now gazing at her with two falsely passionate eyes.

"Princess, do you love me?" he asked all of a sudden, in a voice full of emotion.

"What about you?" she replied, with remarkable assurance. Then, as if overcome by a temptation too strong to be resisted, she stretched out her arm and placed her hand on the back of the young man's neck. "What about you?" she repeated.

Ripandelli threw a glance at the closed door; they must have begun dancing again now, he could hear the rhythmic tumult down below.

"My dear," he answered slowly, "I long for you, it's driving me crazy, I'm incapable of thinking or speaking sensibly . . ." There was a knock at the door; and then the door opened and Lucini, Micheli, Mastrogiovanni and a fourth man of the name of Jancovich burst into the room. This unexpected fourth was the oldest member of the club, a man of about fifty and already going grey; in figure he was ungainly, with a long, lean, melancholy face, a thin nose, and two deep, ironical furrows running down his face from his eyes to his neck. An industrialist, he made a lot of money; he spent the greater part of the day at the tennis club, playing cards; and at the club even the younger men called him by his Christian name, Beniamino. Now, as soon as Jancovich saw Ripandelli and the Princess, he gave, as had been arranged beforehand, a cry of pain and raised his arms above his head.

"What? My son here? And with a woman? And, what's more, with the woman I love?"

Ripandelli turned towards the Princess. "Here's my father," he said; "we're lost!"

"Get out of here!" went on Jancovich in his colourless voice; "get out of here, you unnatural boy!"

"Father," answered Ripandelli naughtily, "there is only one voice I shall obey, the voice of passion."

"And you, my love," went on Jancovich, turning with a sad, dignified expression towards the Princess, "don't let yourself be taken in by this rogue of a son of mine, come to me instead, and lean that charming little head on the breast of your Beniamino, who has never ceased to love you."

Biting his lips hard to prevent himself from laughing, Ripandelli flung himself upon his so-called father, crying out: "You call me a rogue, do you?" There followed a fine scene of wrath and confusion. Jancovich on one side, Ripandelli on the other, held back with difficulty by their friends, pretended to make every possible effort to get at one another and come to blows; cries of "Hold them, hold them, or they'll kill each other" rose above the tumult, together with ill-suppressed bursts of laughter; while the Princess, terrified, cowered back into a corner, her hands clasped together. At last it became possible to calm the two raging antagonists.

"There's nothing to be done about it," said Lucini, stepping forward. "Father and son in love with the same woman: the only thing is for the Princess to make her choice."

So the Princess was asked to give judgment. Undecided, flattered, worried, she came out of her corner with her usual swaying walk, one foot pointing this way, the other that. "I can't choose," she said finally, after a close examination of the two competitors, "because . . . because I like you both."

There was laughter and applause. "And me, Princess—do you like me?" asked Lucini suddenly, taking her round the waist. This was the signal for a kind of orgy: father and son were reconciled and embraced each other; the Princess was made to sit down in the middle of them and an abundance of drink was pressed upon her. In a few minutes she was quite tipsy: she was laughing and clapping her hands, and her hair, standing out round her face, made her head look enormous.

The men started asking her sly questions. "Somebody told me," said Micheli at a certain moment, "that you're not a princess, that you're really nothing at all, just the daughter of some little pork-butcher: is that true?"

She was indignant. "That was a slander, and no doubt whoever told you was the son of a pork-butcher himself . . . I'd have you know that before the War there was actually a Prince of the blood who sent me a marvellous bunch of orchids, with a note; and the note said: 'To my dear little Adelina from her Gogo . . . .'"

These words were received with shouts of laughter. These five men—who allowed their mistresses, in private, to call them by such names as Nini and Lulu, my little cherub or my little piggy-wig—seemed to consider the nickname of Gogo, the pet name of Adelina, as being the height of absurdity and stupidity; they held their sides, they ached with laughing. "Ah Gogo, naughty Gogo," they kept on saying. The Princess, intoxicated and highly flattered, distributed smiles and glances and taps with her eyeglass in every direction. "Oh Princess, how funny you are!" shouted Lucini right in her face, and she—just as though he had paid her a compliment—laughed. "Oh Princess, my Princess," sang Ripandelli sentimentally; but all of a sudden his face hardened: he put out his hand and mercilessly grasped her breast. Red in the face, she struggled to free herself, but next moment suddenly laughed again and cast such a glance at the young man that he at once released his hold. "Ugh, what a flabby breast," he cried to the others, "it's just like squeezing a rag . . . . What about undressing her?" Now that the programme of jokes was more or less at an end, this proposal met with great success. "Princess," said Lucini, "we've been told that you have an extremely beautiful figure . . . . Well now, be generous and let us see it. Then we'll die content."

"Come on, Princess," said Jancovich, in his serious, bleating voice; and without more ado he put his hands on her and started trying to pull the shoulder-straps of her dress down over her arms. "We can't allow you to keep your lovely body hidden any longer . . . that lovely little pink and white body, all full of dimples like the body of a little girl of six . . . ."

"Oh, you shameless creatures!" said the Princess, laughing. But, after a great deal of insistence, she consented to lower her dress half-way down her bosom: her eyes were shining, and the corners of her mouth were trembling with pleasure.

"It's true I have a nice figure, isn't it?" she said to Ripandelli. But the young man made a grimace, and the other exclaimed that it was not enough, they wanted to see more; and Lucini gave a tug at the top of her dress. Then—whether it was that she became ashamed of displaying her already middle-aged body, or that a flash of consciousness, penetrating the fumes of wine, showed her to herself as she actually was, flushed and dishevelled, her breast half bared, surrounded by brutalized men in that little white room—all of a sudden she began to resist and to struggle: "Leave me alone, I tell you, leave me alone," she commanded, trying to release herself. But the sport had excited the five men. Two held her by the arms, while the other three pulled her dress right down to her waist, exposing a torso yellowish and puckered, with flabby, sallow breasts.

"God, how ugly she is!" exclaimed Micheli; "and what a lot of clothes she's got on! She's all bundled up with clothes . . . . She must have at least four pairs of drawers on . . . ." The others were laughing, exhilarated by the spectacle of this unattractive, angry nakedness, and were trying to free her hips of their encumbering mass of clothes. This was not easy, for the Princess was struggling violently; the crimson face beneath the fleece of hair was pitiable, so clearly did it express terror, desperation and shame. But this resistance on her part, instead of moving Ripandelli to pity, irritated him like the spasms of a wounded beast that refuses to die. "You ugly bitch, are you going to stay still or not?" he shouted at her suddenly, and, to give force to his words, he took a champagne-glass from the table and dashed the iced wine over the unfortunate woman's face and chest. The abrupt aspersion gave rise to a plaintive, bitter cry and a frenzied burst of resistance. Somehow or other she managed to free herself from the hands of her tormentors and, naked to the waist, waving her arms above her head, her hair darting out like flames, a disordered mass of clothes trailing downwards from her hips, she hurled herself towards the door.

Astonishment, for one moment, prevented the five men from acting. But Ripandelli shouted: "Catch her or she'll be out in the gallery!" and they threw themselves, all five of them, upon the woman, whose escape had been barred by a precautionary locking of the door. Micheli seized her by one arm, Mastrogiovanni round the waist, Ripandelli actually by the hair. They dragged her back again to the table. Her resistance had infuriated them, and they felt a cruel desire to beat her, to stick pins into her, to torment her. "Now we want you naked," shouted Ripandelli into her face; "naked—that's how we want you." She stared at him with terrified eyes, still struggling; then, all at once, she began to scream.

First she uttered a hoarse cry, then another like a sob, and finally, unexpectedly, a third of extreme shrillness, a piercing "Ay-eee!" Micheli and Mastrogiovanni, frightened, let go of her. As for Ripandelli, possibly it was only at that moment that he became conscious, for the first time, of the seriousness of the situation in which, with his companions, he had become involved. It was as though an enormous hand had squeezed his heart—with all five fingers, as one squeezes a sponge. A terrible rage came over him, a bloody hatred for this woman who had now flung herself against the door again; shouting, he showered blows upon her with his fists, and he himself, at the same time, was smitten with a black sense of hopelessness, with the kind of anguish that says, "There's nothing to be done, the worst has happened, better accept the inevitable . . . ." He had a moment's hesitation; then, with a hand that did not seem to belong to him, so independent of his will-power did it appear, he seized the empty bottle from the table and brought it down with his full strength, just once, on the nape of her neck.

She sank to the floor across the doorway, in a manner that left no doubt as to the efficacy of the blow, and lay on her right side, her forehead against the closed door, her clothes spread round her like a heap of rags. Standing near her, the bottle still in his hand, Ripandelli concentrated the whole of his attention upon her back. At the level of her armpit there was a mole the size of a lentil; this detail, and perhaps also the fact that her thick mass of hair rendered her face invisible, made him imagine, for a second, that he had struck someone quite different and for a quite different reason—for instance some splendid-looking girl with a perfect figure whom he had loved too dearly and in vain and upon whose inanimate limbs he would throw himself weeping and remorseful, bitterly remorseful, and whom it might perhaps be possible to bring back to life. But then the torso gave a strange jerk and abruptly turned over on its back, showing the woman's bosom with one breast falling in each direction and—horrible sight—her face. Her hair concealed her eyes ("luckily", he thought), but her mouth, half-open in a curiously expressionless way, reminded him all too vividly of certain slaughtered animals that he had seen as a child. "She's dead," he thought calmly, at the same time frightened by his own calmness. Then he turned and put the bottle back on the table.

The other four, who had sat down at the far end of the room by the window, looked at him uncomprehendingly. The table in the middle of the room prevented them from having a clear view of the Princess's body; they had seen only the blow. Then, with a kind of cautious curiosity, Lucini rose and, leaning forward, looked towards the door. The thing was there, across the threshold. His companions saw him turn pale. "This time we've gone a bit too far," he said in a low frightened voice, without looking at them.

Micheli, who was sitting in the farthest corner, rose to his feet. He was a medical student, and his privileged position in this respect gave him, as it were, a feeling of responsibility. "Perhaps she's only fainted," he said in a clear voice; "we must bring her round . . . wait a moment." He took a half-full glass from the table and bent over the woman's body, while the others formed a group round him. They watched him as he passed his arm under her back, then lifted her and shook her, and poured a little wine between her lips. But her head swung from side to side, her arms hung lifelessly from her shoulders. Micheli laid her down on the floor again and put his ear to her chest. After a moment he raised himself again. "I think she's dead," he said, still flushed from the effort he had made.

There was silence. "For God's sake cover her up!" suddenly cried Lucini, unable to take his eyes from the body.

"Cover her up yourself!"

Again there was silence. From down below the sound of the band came distinctly to their ears; but now it was more subdued, it must be a tango they were playing. The five men looked at each other. Of them all, only Ripandelli was now sitting down. He was staring straight ahead of him, his shoulders bent, his head in his hands; he could see the black trousers of his friends forming a circle round him, but they were not close enough together, so that it was impossible not to see, through the spaces between them, the prostrate mass of the body lying against the white-painted door at the other side of the room.

"What a mad thing to do," began Mastrogiovanni as though protesting against some ridiculous idea, turning at the same time to Ripandelli; "with the bottle! . . . What ever came over you at that moment?"

"I had nothing to do with it," said someone in a trembling voice. Ripandelli, without moving, knew it was Lucini who spoke. "You're all witnesses that I was sitting over at the window."

It was Jancovich, the oldest of them all, with his melancholy face and flat voice, who answered him. "Yes, yes," he said; "argue the point, my dear chaps, as to who it was and who it wasn't . . . . Then right in the middle of this interesting discussion someone will come in and we shall all go and finish our argument in some other place."

"Well, we shall go there in any case," said Ripandelli sombrely.

Jancovich made a gesture both violent and comic. "This chap's mad," he said. "Just because he himself wants to go to prison, he wants everyone else to go there too." For a brief instant the whole of his thin face was deeply furrowed by laughter. "Now just listen to what I say."

"???"

"Well now . . . . The Princess lived alone, didn't she? So it will be a week or so before her disappearance is noticed . . . . We'll go down now and dance, and behave as if nothing had happened. When the ball is over, we'll get her into my car and take her right away somewhere, outside the town . . . or perhaps we could throw her into the river. Then it'll be thought that she killed herself. She lived all alone . . . in a moment of depression . . . these things do happen. In any case, if people ask us where she is, we'll say that she left the room at a certain moment and has not been seen since. Are we all agreed?"

The others turned pale with fear. The woman was dead—that they knew; but the idea of having committed a crime, of having killed someone, and of being on that account in a state of guilt, had not yet entered their minds. They felt they were Ripandelli's accomplices merely in the matter of amusement, not of murder. The suggestion that the corpse should be thrown into the river brought them abruptly face to face with reality. Lucini, Micheli and Mastrogiovanni protested, declaring that they had nothing to do with it, that they did not wish to have anything to do with it, that Ripandelli must extricate himself as best he could.

"All right then," answered Jancovich, who had been mentally calculating the legal possibilities of the position, "that means that we shall all meet again in court: Ripandelli will be found guilty of murder, but we none the less shall get a few years each as accessories to the crime." They were silent, in consternation. Lucini, who was the youngest of them all, was white in the face, and his eyes were filled with tears. Suddenly he shook his fist in the air. "I knew it would end like this," he cried; "I knew it . . . . Oh, if only I had never come!"

But it was only too evident that Jancovich was right. They had to come to a decision: at any moment someone might come in. The opinion of the oldest man present was approved, and, all of a sudden, as though they wished to stifle thought by action, all five of them started with alacrity to eliminate all traces of the crime. The bottle and glasses were locked up in a cupboard; the corpse was dragged, not without difficulty, into a corner and covered with a large towel; there was a small looking-glass on the wall and each of them went over and examined himself to see if he was clean and tidy. Then, one after the other, they left the room; the light was turned off, the door locked and the key taken by Jancovich.

The ball, at that moment, was at the height of its brilliance. The room was crowded, there were clustering groups of people seated round the walls; others were perching on the windowsills; in the middle the multitude of dancers swirled hither and thither; a thousand "shooting stars" were flying from every direction and people were pelting each other with little multi-coloured balls of cotton-wool; from each corner came shrill and strident sounds of toy whistles and pasteboard pipes;

balloons of every colour were swaying amongst the paper streamers hanging from the chandelier, and every now and then one of them would explode with a sharp pop as the dancing couples competed for them, struggling to snatch them from one another and crowding round anyone who had preserved his own balloon intact. Laughter, voices, sounds, colours, shapes, the blue clouds of tobacco smoke—all these, to the bemused senses of the five men who leant over the balcony and gazed down from above into the luminous cavern, became fused into the golden haze of an unattainable Arabian Nights festivity, creating the effect of a paradise of irresponsibility and frivolity which to them was lost, for ever lost. Whatever efforts they might make their thoughts drew them back, forced them again into the little room full of lockers, with the wine-glasses on the table, the chairs in disorder, the window shut, and, on the floor in one corner, the corpse. But at last they pulled themselves together and went down the stairs.

"Now I do beg of you," said Jancovich, as a final injunction, "be animated, dance, enjoy yourselves as though nothing had happened." Then, led by Mastrogiovanni, they all five went in and mingled with the crowd, indistinguishable now from the other male dancers who, dressed like them in black and holding their partners in their arms, filed past the platform on which the band played, in the slow rhythm of the dance.

STUDY QUESTIONS

1. Why did the committee members decide to invite the "Princess" to their Gala Ball? Why did they decide to hold the ball in the first place?

2. What is "empathy"? Did any of the characters in this story show any signs of having this trait? Did any of the five committee members have any feelings of empathy for the "Princess"? For each other?

3. What effect does Moravia achieve by having a range of ages among the Committee members?

4. At what point in the proceedings did the men begin to become physically violent? Did something specific trigger this violence or was it the inevitable result of the situation?

5. What seems to be Ripandelli's motivation in hitting the "Princess" with the bottle?

6. Do you think the phrase "mental violence" provides a good description of the actions of the five men during the first part of the scene in the little private room? Point out examples of mental violence. Is sadism a form of mental violence?

7. Where are there instances of sexual gestures used for destructive or punitive purposes?

8. How do the following statements enlarge the meaning of the story?

    ". . . paradise of irresponsibility and frivolity."

    ". . . indistinguishable now from the other male dancers . . . in the slow rhythm of the dance."

9. The original intention of the five men was to "have some fun" or "have a bit of sport." How would you describe humor of this sort? Has the author clearly revealed the dangers of such forms of "fun"? Why do you think he did not write a story in which the men were found out and punished for their actions?

12

From THE POSSESSED

Fyodor Dostoevsky

One of the most famous writers in literary history, Fyodor Dostoevsky was born in 1821 and raised in Moscow. His influence on twentieth century writers and thinkers has been a profound one. Among his works are The House of the Dead *(1862),* Notes From the Underground *(1864),* Crime and Punishment *(1866),* The Idiot *(1968),* The Possessed *(1871), and* The Brothers Karamazov *(1879-1880). In* The Possessed, *Dostoevsky offers us a novel of social and intellectual upheavals which foreshadow the events of the Bolshevik revolution 50 years later. The activities of students, intellectuals, and revolutionaries give significant shape to this extraordinarily rich novel. In this selection, Kirillov, a nihilist, gives us unusual reasons for his self-destruction.*

"WELL, THAT'S AN IDEA; of course all are scoundrels; and since life is a beastly thing for a decent man . . . "

"Fool, I am just such a scoundrel as you, as all, not a decent man. There's never been a decent man anywhere."

"He's guessed the truth at last! Can you, Kirillov, with your sense, have failed to see till now that all men are alike, that there are none better or worse, only some are stupider than others, and that if all are scoundrels (which is nonsense, though) there oughtn't to be any people that are not?"

"Ah! Why, you are really in earnest?" Kirillov looked at him with some wonder. "You speak with heat and simply . . . . Can it be that even fellows like you have convictions?"

"Kirillov, I've never been able to understand why you mean to kill yourself. I only know it's from conviction . . . strong conviction. But if you feel a yearning to express yourself, so to say, I am at your service . . . . Only you must think of the time."

"What time is it?"

"Oh, oh, just two." Pyotr Stepanovitch looked at his watch and lighted a cigarette.

"It seems we can come to terms after all," he reflected.

"I've nothing to say to you," muttered Kirillov.

"I remember that something about God comes into it . . . you explained it to me once—twice, in fact. If you shoot yourself, you become God; that's it, isn't it?"

"Yes, I become God."

Pyotr Stepanovitch did not even smile; he waited. Kirillov looked at him subtly.

"You are a political impostor and intriguer. You want to lead me on into philosophy and enthusiasm and to bring about a reconciliation so as to disperse my anger, and then, when I am reconciled with you, beg from me a note to say I killed Shatov."

Pyotr Stepanovitch answered with almost natural frankness.

"Well, supposing I am such a scoundrel. But at the last moments does that matter to you, Kirillov? What are we quarrelling about? Tell me, please. You are one sort of man and I am another—what of it? And what's more, we are both . . . "

"Scoundrels."

"Yes, scoundrels if you like. But you know that that's only words."

"All my life I wanted it not to be only words. I lived because I did not want it to be. Even now every day I want it to be not words."

"Well, every one seeks to be where he is best off. The fish . . . that is, every one seeks his own comfort, that's all. That's been a commonplace for ages and ages."

"Comfort, do you say?"

"Oh, it's not worth while quarrelling over words."

"No, you were right in what you said; let it be comfort. God is necessary and so must exist."

"Well, that's all right, then."

"But I know He doesn't and can't."

"That's more likely."

"Surely you must understand that a man with two such ideas can't go on living?"

"Must shoot himself, you mean?"

"Surely you must understand that one might shoot oneself for that alone? You don't understand that there may be a man, one man out of your thousands of millions, one man who won't bear it and does not want to."

"All I understand is that you seem to be hesitating . . . . That's very bad."

"Stavrogin, too, is consumed by an idea," Kirillov said gloomily, pacing up and down the room. He had not noticed the previous remark.

"What?" Pyotr Stepanovitch pricked up his ears. "What idea? Did he tell you something himself?"

"No, I guessed it myself: if Stavrogin has faith, he does not believe that he has faith. If he hasn't faith, he does not believe that he hasn't."

"Well, Stavrogin has got something else wiser than that in his head," Pyotr Stepanovitch muttered peevishly, uneasily watching the turn the conversation had taken and the pallor of Kirillov.

"Damn it all, he won't shoot himself!" he was thinking. "I always suspected it; it's a maggot in the brain and nothing more; what a rotten lot of people!"

"You are the last to be with me; I shouldn't like to part on bad terms with you," Kirillov vouchsafed suddenly.

Pyotr Stepanovitch did not answer at once. "Damn it all, what is it now?" he thought again.

"I assure you, Kirillov, I have nothing against you personally as a man, and always . . . "

"You are a scoundrel and a false intellect. But I am just the same as you are, and I will shoot myself while you will remain living."

"You mean to say, I am so abject that I want to go on living."

He could not make up his mind whether it was judicious to keep up such a conversation at such a moment or not, and resolved "to be guided by circumstances." But the tone of superiority and of contempt for him, which Kirillov had never disguised, had always irritated him, and now for some reason it irritated him more than ever—possibly because Kirillov, who was to die within an hour or so (Pyotr Stepanovitch still reckoned upon this), seemed to him, as it were, already only half a man, some creature whom he could not allow to be haughty.

"You seem to be boasting to me of your shooting yourself."

"I've always been surprised at everyone's going on living," said Kirillov, not hearing his remark.

"H'm! Admitting that's an idea, but . . ."

"You ape, you assent to get the better of me. Hold your tongue; you won't understand anything. If there is no God, then I am God."

"There, I could never understand that point of yours: why are you God?"

"If God exists, all is His will and from His will I cannot escape. If not, it's all my will and I am bound to show self-will."

"Self-will? But why are you bound?"

"Because all will has become mine. Can it be that no one in the whole planet, after making an end of God and believing in his own will, will dare to express his self-will on the most vital point? It's like a beggar inheriting a fortune and being afraid of it and not daring to approach the bag of gold, thinking himself too weak to own it. I want to manifest my self-will. I may be the only one, but I'll do it."

"Do it by all means."

"I am bound to shoot myself because the highest point of my self-will is to kill myself with my own hands."

"But you won't be the only one to kill yourself; there are lots of suicides."

"With good cause. But to do it without any cause at all, simply for self-will, I am the only one."

"He won't shoot himself," flashed across Pyotr Stepanovitch's mind again.

"Do you know," he observed irritably, "if I were in your place I should kill some one else to show my self-will, not myself. You might be of use. I'll tell you whom, if you are not afraid. Then you needn't shoot yourself today, perhaps. We may come to terms."

"To kill some one would be the lowest point of self-will, and you show your whole soul in that. I am not you: I want the highest point and I'll kill myself."

"He's come to it of himself," Pyotr Stepanovitch muttered malignantly.

"I am bound to show my unbelief," said Kirillov, walking about the room. "I have no higher idea than disbelief in God. I have all the history of mankind on my side. Man has done nothing but invent God so as to go on living, and not kill himself; that's the whole of universal history up till now. I am the first one in the whole history of mankind who would not invent God. Let them know it once for all."

"He won't shoot himself," Pyotr Stepanovitch thought anxiously.

"Let whom know it?" he said, egging him on. "It's only you and me here; you mean Liputin?"

"Let every one know; all will know. There is nothing secret that will not be made known. *He* said so."

And he pointed with feverish enthusiasm to the image of the Saviour, before which a lamp was burning. Pyotr Stepanovitch lost his temper completely.

"So you still believe in Him and you've lighted the lamp; 'to be on the safe side,' I suppose?"

The other did not speak.

"Do you know, to my thinking, you believe perhaps more thoroughly than any priest."

"Believe in whom? In *Him*? Listen." Kirillov stood still, gazing before him with fixed and ecstatic look. "Listen to a great idea: there was a day on earth, and in the midst of the earth there stood three crosses. One on the Cross had such faith that he said to another, 'To-day thou shalt be with me in Paradise.' The day ended; both died and passed away and found neither Paradise nor resurrection. His words did not come true. Listen: that Man was the loftiest of all on earth, He was that which gave meaning to life. The whole planet, with everything on it, is mere madness without that Man. There has never been any like Him before or since, never, up to a miracle. For that is the miracle, that there never was or never will be another like Him. And if that is so, if the laws of nature did not spare even Him, have not spared even their miracle and made even Him live in a lie and die for a lie, then all the planet is a lie and rests on a lie and on mockery. So then, the very laws of the planet are a lie and the vaudeville of devils. What is there to live for? Answer, if you are a man."

"That's a different matter. It seems to me you've mixed up two different causes, and that's a very unsafe thing to do. But excuse me, if you are God? If the lie were ended and if you realised that all the falsity comes from the belief in that former God?"

"So at last you understand!" cried Kirillov rapturously. "So it can be understood if even a fellow like you understands. Do you understand now that the salvation for all consists in proving this idea to every one? Who will prove it? I! I can't understand how an atheist could know that there is no God and not kill himself on the spot. To recognise that there is no God and not to recognise at the same instant that one is God oneself is an absurdity, else one would certainly kill oneself. If you recognise it you are sovereign, and then you won't kill yourself but will live in the greatest glory. But one, the first, must kill himself, for else who will begin and prove it? So I must certainly kill myself, to begin and prove it. Now I am only a god against my will and I am unhappy, because I am *bound* to assert my will. All are unhappy because all are afraid to express their will. Man has hitherto been so unhappy and so poor because he has been afraid to assert his will in the highest point and has shown his self-will only in little things, like a schoolboy. I am awfully unhappy, for I'm awfully afraid. Terror is the curse of man . . . . But I will assert my will, I am bound to believe that I don't believe. I will begin and will make an end of it and open the door, and will save. That's the only thing that will save mankind and will re-create the next generation physically; for with his present physical nature man can't get on without his former God, I believe. For three years I've been seeking for the attribute of my godhead and I've found it; the attribute of my godhead is self-will! That's all I can do to prove in the highest point my independence and my new terrible freedom. For it is very terrible. I am killing myself to prove my independence and my new terrible freedom."

His face was unnaturally pale, and there was a terribly heavy look in his eyes. He was like a man in delirium. Pyotr Stepanovitch thought he would drop on to the floor.

"Give me the pen!" Kirillov cried suddenly, quite unexpectedly, in a positive frenzy. "Dictate; I'll sign anything. I'll sign that I killed Shatov even. Dictate while it amuses me. I am not afraid of what the haughty slaves will think! You will see for youself that all that is secret shall be made manifest! And you will be crushed . . . . I believe, I believe!"

Pyotr Stepanovitch jumped up from his seat and instantly handed him an inkstand and paper, and began dictating, seizing the moment, quivering with anxiety.

"I, Alexey Kirillov, declare . . . "

"Stay; I won't! To whom am I declaring it?"

Kirillov was shaking as though he were in a fever. This declaration and the sudden strange idea of it seemed to absorb him entirely, as though it were a means of escape by which his tortured spirit strove for a moment's relief.

"To whom am I declaring it? I want to know to whom?"

"To no one, every one, the first person who reads it. Why define it? The whole world!"

"The whole world! Bravo! And I won't have any repentance. I don't want penitence and I don't want it for the police!"

"No, of course, there's no need of it, damn the police! Write, if you are in earnest!" Pyotr Stepanovitch cried hysterically.

"Stay! I want to put at the top a face with the tongue out."

"Ech, what nonsense," cried Pyotr Stepanovitch crossly, "you can express all that without the drawing, by—the tone."

"By the tone? That's true. Yes, by the tone, by the tone of it. Dictate, the tone."

"I, Alexey Kirillov," Pyotr Stepanovitch dictated firmly and peremptorily, bending over Kirillov's shoulder and following every letter which the latter formed with a hand trembling with excitement, "I, Kirillov, declare that to-day, the ——th October, at about eight o'clock in the evening, I killed the student Shatov in the park for turning traitor and giving information of the manifestoes and of Fedka, who has been lodging with us for ten days in Filipov's house. I am shooting myself to-day with my revolver, not because I repent and am afraid of you, but because when I was abroad I made up my mind to put an end to my life."

"Is that all?" cried Kirillov with surprise and indignation.

"Not another word," cried Pyotr Stepanovitch, waving his hand, attempting to snatch the document from him.

"Stay." Kirillov put his hand firmly on the paper. "Stay, it's nonsense! I want to say with whom I killed him. Why Fedka? And what about the fire? I want it all and I want to be abusive in tone, too, in tone!"

"Enough, Kirillov, I assure you it's enough," cried Pyotr Stepanovitch almost imploringly, trembling lest he should tear up that paper; "that they may believe you, you must say it as obscurely as possible, just like that, simply in hints. You must only give them a peep of the truth, just enough to tantalise them. They'll tell a story better than ours, and of course they'll believe themselves more than they would us; and you know, it's better than anything—better than anything! Let me have it, it's splendid as it is; give it to me, give it to me!"

And he kept trying to snatch the paper. Kirillov listened open-eyed and appeared to be trying to reflect, but he seemed beyond under-standing now.

"Damn it all," Pyotr Stepanovitch cried all at once, ill-humouredly, "he hasn't signed it! Why are you staring like that? Sign!"

"I want to abuse them," muttered Kirillov. He took the pen, however, and signed. "I want to abuse them."

"Write *'Vive la republique,'* and that will be enough."

"Bravo!" Kirillov almost bellowed with delight. *'Vive la republique democratique sociale et universelle ou la mort!'* No, no, that's not it. *'Liberte, egalite, fraternite ou la mort.'* There, that's better, that's better." He wrote it gleefully under his signature.

"Enough, enough," repeated Pyotr Stepanovitch.

"Stay, a little more. I'll sign it again in French, you know. *'De Kirilloff, gentilhomme russe et citoyen du monde.'* Ha ha!" He went off in a peal of laughter. "No, no, no; stay. I've found something better than all. Eureka! *'Gentilhomme, seminariste russe et citoyen du monde civilise!'* That's better than any . . . ." He jumped up from the sofa and suddenly, with a rapid gesture, snatched up the revolver from the window, ran with it into the next room, and closed the door behind him. Pyotr Stepanovitch stood for a moment, pondering and gazing at the door.

"If he does it at once, perhaps he'll do it, but if he begins thinking, nothing will come of it."

Meanwhile he took up the paper, sat down, and looked at it again. The wording of the document pleased him again.

"What's needed for the moment? What's wanted is to throw them all off the scent and keep them busy for a time. The park? There's no park in the town and they'll guess its Skvoreshniki of themselves. But while they are arriving at that, time will be passing; then the search will take time too; then when they find the body it will prove that the story is true, and it will follow that's it all true, that it's true about Fedka too. And Fedka explains the fire, the Lebyadkins; so that it was all being hatched here, at Filipov's, while they overlooked it and saw nothing—that will quite turn their heads! They will never think of the quintet; Shatov and Kirillov and Fedka and Lebyadkin, and why they killed each other—that will be another question for them. Oh, damn it all, I don't hear the shot!"

Though he had been reading and admiring the wording of it, he had been listening anxiously all the time, and he suddenly flew into a rage. He looked anxiously at his watch; it was getting late and it was fully ten minutes since Kirillov had gone out . . . . Snatching up the candle, he went to the door of the room where Kirillov had shut himself up. He was just at the door when the thought struck him that the candle had burnt out, that it would not last another twenty minutes, and that there was no other in the room. He took hold the handle and listened warily; he did not hear the slightest sound. He suddenly opened the door and lifted up the candle: something uttered a roar and rushed at him. He slammed the door with all his might and pressed his weight against it; but all sounds died away and again there was deathlike stillness.

He stood for a long while irresolute, with the candle in his hand. He had been able to see very little in the second he held the door open, but he had a glimpse of the face of Kirillov standing at the other end of the room by the window, and the savage fury with which the latter had rushed upon him. Pyotr Stepanovitch started, rapidly set the candle on the table, made ready his revolver, and retreated on tiptoe to the farthest corner of the room, so that if Kirillov opened the door and rushed up to the table with the revolver he would still have time to be the first to aim and fire.

Pyotr Stepanovitch had by now lost all faith in the suicide. "He was standing in the middle of the room, thinking," flashed like a whirlwind through Pyotr Stepanovitch's mind, "and the room was dark and horrible too . . . . He roared and rushed at me. There are two possibilities: either I interrupted him at the very second when he was pulling the trigger or . . . or he was standing planning how to kill me. Yes, that's it, he was planning it . . . . He knows I won't go away without killing him if he funks it himself—so that he would have to kill me first to prevent my killing him . . . . And again, again there is silence. I am really frightened: he may open the door all of a sudden . . . . The nuisance of it is that he believes in God like any priest . . . . He won't shoot himself for anything! There are lots of these people nowadays 'who've come to it of themselves.' A rotten lot! Oh, damn it, the candle, the candle! It'll go out within a quarter of an hour for certain . . . . I must put a stop to it; come what may, I must put a stop to it . . . . Now I can kill him . . . . With that document here no one would think of my killing him. I can put him in such an attitude on the floor with an unloaded revolver in his hand that they'd be certain he'd done it himself . . . . Ach, damn it! how is one to kill him? If I open the door he'll rush out again and shoot me first. Damn it all, he'll be sure to miss!"

He was in agonies, trembling at the necessity of action and his own indecision. At last he took up the candle and again approached the door with the revolver held up in readiness; he put his left hand, in which he held the candle, on the door-handle. But he managed awkwardly: the handle clanked, there was a rattle and a creak. "He will fire straightway," flashed through Pyotr Stepanovitch's mind. With his foot he flung the door open violently, raised the candle, and held out the revolver; but no shot nor cry came from within . . . . There was no one in the room.

He started. The room led nowhere. There was no exit, no means of escape from it. He lifted the candle higher and looked about him more attentively: there was certainly no one. He called Kirillov's name in a low voice, then again louder; no one answered.

"Can he have got out by the window?" The casement in one window was, in fact, open. "Absurd! He couldn't have got away through the casement." Pyotr Stepanovitch crossed the room and went up to the window. "He couldn't possibly." All at once he turned round quickly and was aghast at something extraordinary.

Against the wall facing the windows on the right of the door stood a cupboard. On the right side of this cupboard, in the corner formed by the cupboard and the wall, stood Kirillov, and he was standing in a very strange way; motionless, perfectly erect, with his arms held stiffly at his sides, his head raised and pressed tightly back against the wall in the very corner, he seemed to be trying to conceal and efface himself. Everything seemed to show that he was hiding, yet somehow it was not easy to believe it. Pyotr Stepanovitch was standing a little sideways to the corner, and could only see the projecting parts of the figure. He could not bring himself to move to the left to get a full view of Kirillov and solve the mystery. His heart began beating violently, and he felt a sudden rush of blind fury: he started from where he stood, and shouting and stamping with his feet, he rushed to the horrible place.

But when he reached Kirillov he stopped short again, still more overcome, horror-stricken. What struck him most was that, in spite of his shout and his furious rush, the figure did not stir, did not move a single limb—as though it were of stone or of wax. The pallor of the face was unnatural, the black eyes were quite unmoving and were staring away at a point in the distance. Pyotr Stepanovitch lowered the candle and raised it again, lighting up the figure from all points of view and scrutinising it. He suddenly noticed that, although Kirillov was looking straight before him, he could see him and was perhaps watching him out of the corner of his eye. Then the idea occurred to him to hold the candle right up to the wretch's face, to scorch him and see what he would do. He suddenly fancied that Kirillov's chin twitched and that something like a mocking smile passed over his lips—as though he had guessed Pyotr Stepanovitch's thought. He shuddered and, beside himself, clutched violently at Kirillov's shoulder.

Then something happened so hideous and so soon over that Pyotr Stepanovitch could never afterwards recover a coherent impression of it. He had hardly touched Kirillov when the latter bent down quickly and with his head knocked the candle out of Pyotr Stepanovitch's hand; the candlestick fell with a clang on the ground and the candle went out. At the same moment he was conscious of a fearful pain in the little finger of his left hand. He cried out, and all that he could remember was that, beside himself, he hit out with all his might and struck three blows with the revolver on the head of Kirillov, who had bent down to him and had bitten his finger. At last he tore away his finger and rushed headlong to get out of the house, feeling his way in the dark. He was pursued by terrible shouts from the room.

"Directly, directly, directly, directly." Ten times. But he still ran on, and was running into the porch when he suddenly heard a loud shot. Then he stopped short in the dark porch and stood deliberating for five minutes; at last he made his way back into the house. But he had to get the candle. He had only to feel on the floor on the right of the cupboard for the candlestick; but how was he to light the candle? There suddenly came into his mind a vague recollection: he recalled that when he had run into the kitchen the day before to attack Fedka he had noticed in passing a large red box of matches in a corner on a shelf. Feeling with his hands, he made his way to the door on the left leading to the kitchen, found it, crossed the passage, and went down the steps. On the shelf, on the very spot where he had just recalled seeing it, he felt in the dark a full unopened box of matches. He hurriedly went up the steps again without striking a light, and it was only when he was near the cupboard, at the spot where he had struck Kirillov with the revolver and been bitten by him, that he remembered his bitten finger, and at the same instant was conscious that it was unbearably painful. Clenching his teeth, he managed somehow to light the candle-end, set it in the candlestick again, and looked about him: near the open casement, with his feet towards the right-hand corner, lay the dead body of Kirillov. The shot had been fired at the right temple and the bullet had come out at the top of the left, shattering the skull. There were splashes of blood and brains. The revolver was still in the suicide's hand on the floor. Death must have been instantaneous. After a careful look around, Pyotr Stepanovitch got up and went out on tiptoe, closed the door, left the candle on the table in the outer room, thought a moment, and resolved not to put it out, reflecting that it could not possibly set fire to anything. Looking once more at the document left on the table, he smiled mechanically and then went out of the house, still for some reason walking on tiptoe. He crept through Fedka's hole again and carefully replaced the posts after him.

STUDY QUESTIONS

1. What seems to be the motivation for Kirillov's suicide?
2. Differentiate the views of Pyotr Stepanovitch and Alexey Kirillov. In what ways are they similar?
3. What is Kirillov's view of Jesus? Summarize Kirillov's arguments about God and existence. How does Kirillov propose to save mankind by killing himself?
4. What support can you give to Stavrogin's statement that Kirillov "believes in God like any priest"?
5. What metaphysical reason can one give for suicide? What psychological reasons? Are the two related?

13

A GOOD MAN IS HARD TO FIND*

Flannery O'Connor

Born in Savannah, Georgia in 1925, of Catholic parents, Flannery O'Connor attended parochial school and Georgia Woman's College in Milledgeville. Her first novel, Wise Blood, *was published in 1952. Both her collection of short stories,* A Good Man Is Hard to Find, *and a novel,* The Violent Bear It Away, *were published in 1955. This story of a middleclass family stranded on a highway and of its encounter with psychotic killers takes us into some of the darker tributaries of violence.*

THE GRANDMOTHER didn't want to go to Florida. She wanted to visit some of her connections in east Tennessee and she was seizing at every chance to change Bailey's mind. Bailey was the son she lived with, her only boy. He was sitting on the edge of his chair at the table, bent over the orange sports section of the *Journal.* "Now look here, Bailey," she said, "see here, read this," and she stood with one hand on her thin hip and the other rattling the newspaper at his bald head. "Here this fellow that calls himself The Misfit is aloose from the Federal Pen and headed toward Florida and you read here what it says he did to these people. Just you read it. I wouldn't take my children in any direction with a criminal like that aloose in it. I couldn't answer to my conscience if I did."

Bailey didn't look up from his reading so she wheeled around then and faced the children's mother, a young woman in slacks, whose face was as broad and innocent as a cabbage and was tied around with a green head-kerchief that had two points on the top like rabbit's ears. She was sitting on the sofa, feeding the baby his apricots out of a jar. "The children have been to Florida before," the old lady said. "You all ought to take them somewhere else for a change so they would see different parts of the world and be broad. They never have been to east Tennessee."

The children's mother didn't seem to hear her but the eight-year-old boy, John Wesley, a stocky child with glasses, said, "If you don't want to go to Florida, why dontcha stay at home?" He and the little girl, June Star, were reading the funny papers on the floor.

"She wouldn't stay at home to be queen for a day," June Star said without raising her yellow head.

"Yes and what would you do if this fellow, The Misfit, caught you?" the grandmother asked.

"I'd smack his face," John Wesley said.

"She wouldn't stay at home for a million bucks," June Star said. "Afraid she'd miss something. She has to go everywhere we go."

"All right, Miss," the grandmother said. "Just remember that the next time you want me to curl your hair."

June Star said her hair was naturally curly.

The next morning the grandmother was the first one in the car, ready to go. She had her big black valise that looked like the head of a hippopotamus in one corner, and underneath it she was hiding a basket with Pitty Sing, the cat, in it. She didn't intend for the cat to be left alone in the house for three days because he would miss her too much and she was afraid he might brush against one of the gas burners and accidentally asphyxiate himself. Her son, Bailey, didn't like to arrive at a motel with a cat.

She sat in the middle of the back seat with John Wesley and June Star on either side of her. Bailey and the children's mother and the baby sat in front and they left Atlanta at eight forty-five with the mileage on the car at 55890. The grandmother wrote this down because she thought it would be interesting to say how many miles they had been when they got back. It took them twenty minutes to reach the outskirts of the city.

The old lady settled herself comfortably, removing her white cotton gloves and putting them up with her purse on the shelf in front of the back window. The children's mother still had on slacks and still had her head tied up in a green kerchief, but the grandmother had on a navy blue straw sailor hat with a bunch of white violets on the brim and a navy blue dress with a small white dot in the print. Her collars and cuffs were white organdy trimmed with lace and at her neckline she had pinned a purple spray of cloth violets containing a sachet. In case of an accident, anyone seeing her dead on the highway would know at once that she was a lady.

She said she thought it was going to be a good day for driving, neither too hot nor too cold, and she cautioned Bailey that the speed limit was fifty-five miles an hour and that the patrolmen hid themselves behind billboards and small clumps of trees and sped out after you before you had a chance to slow down. She pointed out interesting details of the scenery: Stone Mountain; the blue granite that in some places came up to both sides of the highway; the brilliant red clay banks slightly streaked with purple; and the various crops that made rows of green lace-work on the ground. The trees were full of silver-white sunlight and the meanest of them sparkled. The children were reading comic magazines and their mother had gone back to sleep.

"Let's go through Georgia fast so we won't have to look at it much," John Wesley said.

"If I were a little boy," said the grandmother, "I wouldn't talk about my native state that way. Tennesse has the mountains and Georgia has the hills."

"Tennessee is just a hillbilly dumping ground," John Wesley said, "and Georgia is a lousy state too."

"You said it," June Star said.

"In my time," said the grandmother, folding her thin veined fingers, "children were more respectful of their native states and their parents and everything else. People did right then. Oh look at the cute little pickaninny!" she said and pointed to a Negro child standing in the door of a shack. "Wouldn't that make a picture, now?" she asked and they all turned and looked at the little Negro out of the back window. He waved.

"He didn't have any britches on," June Star said.

"He probably didn't have any," the grandmother explained. "Little niggers in the country don't have things like we do. If I could paint, I'd paint that picture," she said.

The children exchanged comic books.

The grandmother offered to hold the baby and the children's mother passed him over the front seat to her. She set him on her knee and bounced him and told him about the things they were passing. She rolled her eyes and screwed up her mouth and stuck her leathery thin face into his smooth bland one. Occasionally he gave her a far-away smile. They passed a large cotton field with five or six graves fenced in the middle of it, like a small island. "Look at the graveyard!" the grandmother said, pointing it out. "That was the old family burying ground. That belonged to the plantation."

"Where's the plantation?" John Wesley asked.

"Gone With the Wind," said the grandmother. "Ha. Ha."

When the children finished all the comic books they had brought, they opened the lunch and ate it. The grandmother ate a peanut butter sandwich and an olive and would not let the children throw the box and the paper napkins out the window. When there was nothing else to do they played a game by choosing a cloud and making the other two guess what shape it suggested. John Wesley took one the shape of a cow and June Star guessed a cow and John Wesley said, no, an automobile, and June Star said he didn't play fair, and they began to slap each other over the grandmother.

The grandmother said she would tell them a story if they would keep quiet. When she told a story, she rolled her eyes and waved her head and was very dramatic. She said once when she was a maiden lady she had been courted by a Mr. Edgar Atkins Teagarden from Jasper, Georgia. She said he was a very good-looking man and a gentleman and that he brought her a watermelon every Saturday afternoon with his initials cut in it, E. A. T. Well, one Saturday, she said, Mr. Teagarden brought the watermelon and there was nobody at home and he left it on the front porch and returned in his buggy to Jasper, but she never got the watermelon, she said, because a nigger boy ate it when he saw the initials, E. A. T.! This story tickled John Wesley's funny bone and he giggled and giggled but June Star didn't think it was any good. She said she wouldn't marry a man that just brought her a watermelon on Saturday. The grandmother said she would have done well to marry Mr. Teagarden because he was a gentleman and had bought Coca-Cola stock when it first came out and that he had died only a few years ago, a very wealthy man.

They stopped at The Tower for barbecued sandwiches. The Tower was a part stucco and part wood filling station and dance hall set in a clearing outside of Timothy. A fat man named Red Sammy Butts ran it and there were signs stuck here and there on the building and for miles up and down the highway saying, TRY RED SAMMY'S FAMOUS

BARBECUE. NONE LIKE FAMOUS RED SAMMY'S! RED SAM!
THE FAT BOY WITH THE HAPPY LAUGH. A VETERAN! RED
SAMMY'S YOUR MAN!

Red Sammy was lying on the bare ground outside The Tower with
his head under a truck while a gray monkey about a foot high, chained
to a small chinaberry tree, chattered nearby. The monkey sprang back
into the tree and got on the highest limb as soon as he saw the children
jump out of the car and run toward him.

Inside, The Tower was a long dark room with a counter at one end
and tables at the other and dancing space in the middle. They all sat
down at a board table next to the nickelodeon and Red Sam's wife, a
tall burnt-brown woman with hair and eyes lighter than her skin, came
and took their order. The children's mother put a dime in the machine
and played "The Tennessee Waltz," and the grandmother said that tune
always made her want to dance. She asked Bailey if he would like to dance
but he only glared at her. He didn't have a naturally sunny disposition like
she did and trips made him nervous. The grandmother's brown eyes were
very bright. She swayed her head from side to side and pretended she was
dancing in her chair. June Star said play something she could tap to so the
children's mother put in another dime and played a fast number and June
Star stepped out onto the dance floor and did her tap routine.

"Ain't she cute?" Red Sam's wife said, leaning over the counter.
"Would you like to come be my little girl?"

"No I certainly wouldn't," June Star said. "I wouldn't live in a
broken-down place like this for a million bucks!" and she ran back to the
table.

"Ain't she cute?" the woman repeated, stretching her mouth politely.

"Arn't you ashamed?" hissed the grandmother.

Red Sam came in and told his wife to quit lounging on the counter
and hurry up with these people's order. His khaki trousers reached just
to his hip bones and his stomach hung over them like a sack of meal
swaying under his shirt. He came over and sat down at a table nearby
and let out a combination sigh and yodel. "You can't win," he said.
"You can't win," and he wiped his sweating red face off with a gray
handkerchief. "These days you don't know who to trust," he said.
"Ain't that the truth?"

"People are certainly not nice like they used to be," said the
grandmother.

"Two fellers come in here last week," Red Sammy said, "driving a Chrysler. It was a old beat-up car but it was a good one and these boys looked all right to me. Said they worked at the mill and you know I let them fellers charge the gas they bought? Now why did I do that?"

"Because you're a good man!" the grandmother said at once.

"Yes'm, I suppose so," Red Sam said as if he were struck with this answer.

His wife brought the orders, carrying the five plates all at once without a tray, two in each hand and one balanced on her arm. "It isn't a soul in this green world of God's that you can trust," she said. "And I don't count nobody out of that, not nobody," she repeated, looking at Red Sammy.

"Did you read about that criminal, The Misfit, that's escaped?" asked the grandmother.

"I wouldn't be a bit surprised if he didn't attact this place right here," said the woman. "If he hears about it being here, I wouldn't be none surprised to see him. If he hears it's two cent in the cash register, I wouldn't be a tall surprised if he . . ."

"That'll do," Red Sam said. "Go bring these people their Co'-Colas," and the woman went off to get the rest of the order.

"A good man is hard to find," Red Sammy said. "Everything is getting terrible. I remember the day you could go off and leave your screen door unlatched. Not no more."

He and the grandmother discussed better times. The old lady said that in her opinion Europe was entirely to blame for the way things were now. She said the way Europe acted you would think we were made of money and Red Sam said it was no use talking about it, she was exactly right. The children ran outside into the white sunlight and looked at the monkey in the lacy chinaberry tree. He was busy catching fleas on himself and biting each one carefully between his teeth as if it were a delicacy.

They drove off again into the hot afternoon. The grandmother took cat naps and woke up every few minutes with her own snoring. Outside of Toombsboro she woke up and recalled an old plantation that she had visited in this neighborhood once when she was a young lady. She said the house had six white columns across the front and that there was an avenue of oaks leading up to it and two little wooden trellis arbors on either side in front where you sat down with your suitor after a stroll in the garden. She recalled exactly which road to turn off to get to it. She knew that Bailey would not be willing to lose any time looking at an old house, but the more she talked about it, the more she wanted to see it once again and find out if the little twin arbors were still standing. "There was a secret panel in this house," she said craftily, not telling the truth but wishing that she were, "and the story went that all the family silver was hidden in it when Sherman came through but it was never found . . ."

"Hey!" John Wesley said. "Let's go see it! We'll find it! We'll poke all the woodwork and find it! Who lives there? Where do you turn off at? Hey Pop, can't we turn off there?"

"We never have seen a house with a secret panel!" June Star shrieked. "Let's go to the house with the secret panel! Hey Pop, can't we go see the house with the secret panel!"

"It's not far from here, I know," the grandmother said. "It wouldn't take over twenty minutes."

Bailey was looking straight ahead. His jaw was as rigid as a horseshoe. "No," he said.

The children began to yell and scream that they wanted to see the house with the secret panel. John Wesley kicked the back of the front seat and June Star hung over her mother's shoulder and whined desperately into her ear that they never had any fun even on their vacation, that they could never do what THEY wanted to do. The baby began to scream and John Wesley kicked the back of the seat so hard that his father could feel the blows in his kidney.

"All right!" he shouted and drew the car to a stop at the side of the road. "Will you all shut up? Will you all just shut up for one second? If you don't shut up, we won't go anywhere."

"It would be very educational for them," the grandmother murmured.

"All right," Bailey said, "but get this: this is the only time we're going to stop for anything like this. This is the one and only time."

"The dirt road that you have to turn down is about a mile back," the grandmother directed. "I marked it when we passed."

"A dirt road," Bailey groaned.

After they had turned around and were headed toward the dirt road, the grandmother recalled other points about the house, the beautiful glass over the front doorway and the candle-lamp in the hall. John Wesley said that the secret panel was probably in the fireplace.

"You can't go inside this house," Bailey said. "You don't know who lives there."

"While you all talk to the people in front, I'll run around behind and get in a window," John Wesley suggested.

"We'll all stay in the car," his mother said.

They turned onto the dirt road and the car raced roughly along in a swirl of pink dust. The grandmother recalled the times when there were no paved roads and thirty miles was a day's journey. The dirt road was hilly and there were sudden washes in it and sharp curves on dangerous embankments. All at once they would be on a hill, looking down over the blue tops of trees for miles around, then the next minute, they would be in a red depression with the dust-coated trees looking down on them.

"This place had better turn up in a minute," Bailey said, "or I'm going to turn around."

The road looked as if no one had traveled on it in months.

"It's not much farther," the grandmother said and just as she said it, a horrible thought came to her. The thought was so embarrassing that she turned red in the face and her eyes dilated and her feet jumped up, upsetting her valise in the corner. The instant the valise moved, the newspaper top she had over the basket under it rose with a snarl and Pitty Sing, the cat, sprang onto Bailey's shoulder.

The children were thrown to the floor and their mother, clutching the baby, was thrown out the door onto the ground; the old lady was thrown into the front seat. The car turned over once and landed right-side-up in a gulch off the side of the road. Bailey remained in the driver's seat with the cat—gray-striped with a broad white face and an orange nose—clinging to his neck like a caterpillar.

As soon as the children saw they could move their arms and legs, they scrambled out of the car, shouting, "We've had an ACCIDENT!" The grandmother was curled up under the dashboard, hoping she was injured so that Bailey's wrath would not come down on her all at once. The horrible thought she had had before the accident was that the house she had remembered so vividly was not in Georgia but in Tennessee.

Bailey removed the cat from his neck with both hands and flung it out the window against the side of a pine tree. Then he got out of the car and started looking for the children's mother. She was sitting against the side of the red gutted ditch, holding the screaming baby, but she only had a cut down her face and a broken shoulder. "We've had an ACCIDENT!" the children screamed in a frenzy of delight.

"But nobody's killed," June Star said with disappointment as the grandmother limped out of the car, her hat still pinned to her head but the broken front brim standing up at a jaunty angle and the violet spray hanging off the side. They all sat down in the ditch, except the children, to recover from the shock. They were all shaking.

"Maybe a car will come along," said the children's mother hoarsely.

"I believe I have injured an organ," said the grandmother, pressing her side, but no one answered her. Bailey's teeth were clattering. He had on a yellow sport shirt with bright blue parrots designed in it and his face was as yellow as the shirt. The grandmother decided that she would not mention that the house was in Tennessee.

The road was about ten feet above and they could see only the tops of the trees on the other side of it. Behind the ditch they were sitting in there were more woods, tall and dark and deep. In a few minutes they saw a car some distance away on top of a hill, coming slowly as if the occupants were watching them. The grandmother stood up and waved both arms dramatically to attract their attention. The car continued to come on slowly, disappeared around a bend and appeared again, moving even slower, on top of the hill they had gone over. It was a big black battered hearse-like automobile. There were three men in it.

It came to a stop just over them and for some minutes, the driver looked down with a steady expressionless gaze to where they were sitting, and didn't speak. Then he turned his head and muttered something to the other two and they got out. One was a fat boy in black trousers and a red sweat shirt with a silver stallion embossed on the front of it. He moved around on the right side of them and stood staring, his mouth partly open in a kind of loose grin. The other had on khaki pants and a blue striped coat and a gray hat pulled down very low, hiding most of his face. He came around slowly on the left side. Neither spoke.

The driver got out of the car and stood by the side of it, looking down at them. He was an older man than the other two. His hair was just beginning to gray and he wore silver-rimmed spectacles that gave him a scholarly look. He had a long creased face and didn't have on any shirt or undershirt. He had on blue jeans that were too tight for him and was holding a black hat and a gun. The two boys also had guns.

"We've had an ACCIDENT!" the children screamed.

The grandmother had the peculiar feeling that the bespectacled man was someone she knew. His face was as familiar to her as if she had known him all her life but she could not recall who he was. He moved away from the car and began to come down the embankment, placing his feet carefully so that he wouldn't slip. He had on tan and white shoes and no socks, and his ankles were red and thin. "Good afternoon," he said. "I see you all had you a little spill."

"We turned over twice!" said the grandmother.

"Oncet," he corrected. "We seen it happen. Try their car and see will it run, Hiram," he said quietly to the boy with the gray hat.

"What you got that gun for?" John Wesley asked. "Whatcha gonna do with that gun?"

"Lady," the man said to the children's mother, "would you mind calling them children to sit down by you? Children make me nervous. I want all you all to sit down right together there where you're at."

"What are you telling US what to do for?" June Star asked.

Behind them the line of woods gaped like a dark open mouth. "Come here," said their mother.

"Look here now," Bailey began suddenly, "we're in a predicament! We're in . . ."

The grandmother shrieked. She scrambled to her feet and stood staring. "You're The Misfit!" she said. "I recognized you at once!"

"Yes'm," the man said, smiling slightly as if he were pleased in spite of himself to be known, "but it would have been better for all of you, lady, if you hadn't of reckernized me."

Bailey turned his head sharply and said something to his mother that shocked even the children. The old lady began to cry and The Misfit reddened.

"Lady," he said, "don't you get upset. Sometimes a man says things he don't mean. I don't reckon he meant to talk to you thataway."

"You wouldn't shoot a lady, would you?" the grandmother said and removed a clean handkerchief from her cuff and began to slap at her eyes with it.

The Misfit pointed the toe of his shoe into the ground and made a little hole and then covered it up again. "I would hate to have to," he said.

"Listen," the grandmother almost screamed, "I know you're a good man. You don't look a bit like you have common blood. I know you must come from nice people!"

"Yes mam," he said, "finest people in the world." When he smiled he showed a row of strong white teeth. "God never made a finer woman than my mother and my daddy's heart was pure gold," he said. The boy with the red sweat shirt had come around behind them and was standing with his gun at his hip. The Misfit squatted down on the ground. "Watch them children, Bobby Lee," he said. "You know they make me nervous." He looked at the six of them huddled together in front of him and he seemed to be embarrassed as if he couldn't think of anything to say. "Ain't a cloud in the sky," he remarked, looking up at it. "Don't see no sun but don't see no cloud neither."

"Yes, it's a beautiful day," said the grandmother. "Listen," she said, "you shouldn't call yourself The Misfit because I know you're a good man at heart. I can just look at you and tell."

"Hush!" Bailey yelled. "Hush! Everybody shut up and let me handle this!" He was squatting in the position of a runner about to sprint forward but he didn't move.

"I pre-chate that, lady," The Misfit said and drew a little circle in the ground with the butt of his gun.

"It'll take a half a hour to fix this here car," Hiram called, looking over the raised hood of it.

"Well, first you and Bobby Lee get him and that little boy to step over yonder with you," The Misfit said, pointing to Bailey and John Wesley. "The boys want to ast you something," he said to Bailey. "Would you mind stepping back in them woods there with them?"

"Listen," Bailey began, "we're in a terrible predicament! Nobody realizes what this is," and his voice cracked. His eyes were as blue and intense as the parrots in his shirt and he remained perfectly still.

The grandmother reached up to adjust her hat brim as if she were going to the woods with him but it came off in her hand. She stood staring at it and after a second she let it fall on the ground. Hiram pulled Bailey up by the arm as if he were assisting an old man. John Wesley caught hold of his father's hand and Bobby Lee followed. They went off toward the woods and just as they reached the dark edge, Bailey turned and supporting himself against a gray naked pine trunk, he shouted, "I'll be back in a minute, Mamma, wait on me!"

"Come back this instant!" his mother shrilled but they all disappeared into the woods.

"Bailey Boy!" the grandmother called in a tragic voice but she found she was looking at The Misfit squatting on the ground in front of her. "I just know you're a good man," she said desperately. "You're not a bit common!"

"Nome, I ain't a good man," The Misfit said after a second as if he had considered her statement carefully, "but I ain't the worst in the world neither. My daddy said I was a different breed of dog from my brothers and sisters. 'You know,' Daddy said, 'it's some that can live their whole life out without asking about it and it's others has to know why it is, and this boy is one of the latters. He's going to be into everything!'" He put on his black hat and looked up suddenly and then away deep into the woods as if he were embarrassed again. "I'm sorry I don't have on a shirt before you ladies," he said, hunching his shoulders slightly. "We buried our clothes that we had on when we escaped and we're just making do until we can get better. We borrowed these from some folks we met," he explained.

"That's perfectly all right," the grandmother said. "Maybe Bailey has an extra shirt in his suitcase."

"I'll look and see terrectly," The Misfit said.

"Where are they taking him?" the children's mother screamed.

"Daddy was a card himself," The Misfit said. "You couldn't put anything over on him. He never got in trouble with the Authorities though. Just had the knack of handling them."

"You could be honest too if you'd only try," said the grandmother. "Think how wonderful it would be to settle down and live a comfortable life and not have to think about somebody chasing you all the time."

The Misfit kept scratching in the ground with the butt of his gun as if he were thinking about it. "Yes'm, somebody is always after you," he murmured.

The grandmother noticed how thin his shoulder blades were just behind his hat because she was standing up looking down on him. "Do you ever pray?" she asked.

He shook his head. All she saw was the black hat wiggle between his shoulder blades. "Nome," he said.

There was a pistol shot from the woods, followed closely by another. Then silence. The old lady's head jerked around. She could hear the wind move through the tree tops like a long satisfied insuck of breath. "Bailey Boy!" she called.

"I was a gospel singer for a while," The Misfit said. "I been most everything. Been in the arm service, both land and sea, at home and abroad, been twict married, been an undertaker, been with the railroads, plowed Mother Earth, been in a tornado, seen a man burnt alive oncet," and he looked up at the children's mother and the little girl who were sitting close together, their faces white and their eyes glassy; "I even seen a woman flogged," he said.

"Pray, pray," the grandmother began, "pray, pray . . ."

"I never was a bad boy that I remember of," The Misfit said in an almost dreamy voice, "but somewheres along the line I done something wrong and got sent to the penitentiary. I was buried alive," and he looked up and held her attention to him by a steady stare.

"That's when you should have started to pray," she said. "What did you do to get sent to the penitentiary that first time?"

"Turn to the right, it was a wall," The Misfit said, looking up again at the cloudless sky. "Turn to the left, it was a wall. Look up it was a ceiling, look down it was a floor. I forget what I done, lady. I set there and set there, trying to remember what it was I done and I ain't recalled it to this day. Oncet in a while, I would think it was coming to me, but it never come."

"Maybe they put you in by mistake," the old lady said vaguely.

"Nome," he said. "It wasn't no mistake. They had the papers on me."

"You must have stolen something," she said.

The Misfit sneered slightly. "Nobody had nothing I wanted," he said. "It was a head-doctor at the penitentiary said what I had done was kill my daddy but I known that for a lie. My daddy died in nineteen ought nineteen of the epidemic flu and I never had a thing to do with it. He was buried in the Mount Hopewell Baptist churchyard and you can go there and see for yourself."

"If you would pray," the old lady said, "Jesus would help you."

"That's right," The Misfit said.

"Well then, why don't you pray?" she asked trembling with delight suddenly.

"I don't want no hep," he said. "I'm doing all right by myself."

Bobby Lee and Hiram came ambling back from the woods. Bobby Lee was dragging a yellow shirt with bright blue parrots in it.

"Thow me that shirt, Bobby Lee," The Misfit said. The shirt came flying at him and landed on his shoulder and he put it on. The grandmother couldn't name what the shirt reminded her of. "No, lady," The Misfit said while he was buttoning it up, "I found out the crime don't matter. You can do one thing or you can do another, kill a man or take a tire off his car, because sooner or later you're going to forget what it was you done and just be punished for it."

The children's mother had begun to make heaving noises as if she couldn't get her breath. "Lady," he asked, "would you and that little girl like to step off yonder with Bobby Lee and Hiram and join your husband?"

"Yes, thank you," the mother said faintly. Her left arm dangled helplessly and she was holding the baby, who had gone to sleep, in the other. "Hep that lady up, Hiram," The Misfit said as she struggled to climb out of the ditch, "and Bobby Lee, you hold onto that little girl's hand."

"I don't want to hold hands with him," June Star said. "He reminds me of a pig."

The fat boy blushed and laughed and caught her by the arm and pulled her off into the woods after Hiram and her mother.

Alone with The Misfit, the grandmother found that she had lost her voice. There was not a cloud in the sky nor any sun. There was nothing around her but woods. She wanted to tell him that he must pray. She opened and closed her mouth several times before anything came out. Finally she found herself saying, "Jesus. Jesus," meaning, Jesus will help you, but the way she was saying it, it sounded as if she might be cursing.

"Yes'm," The Misfit said as if he agreed. "Jesus thown everything off balance. It was the same case with Him as with me except He hadn't committed any crime and they could prove I had committed one because they had the papers on me. Of course," he said, "they never shown me my papers. That's why I sign myself now. I said long ago, you get you a signature and sign everything you do and keep a copy of it. Then you'll know what you done and you can hold up the crime to the punishment and see do they match and in the end you'll have something to prove you ain't been treated right. I call myself The Misfit," he said, "because I can't make what all I done wrong fit what all I gone through in punishment."

There was a piercing scream from the woods, followed closely by a pistol report. "Does it seem right to you, lady, that one is punished a heap and another ain't punished at all?"

"Jesus!" the old lady cried. "You've got good blood! I know you wouldn't shoot a lady! I know you come from nice people! Pray! Jesus, you ought not to shoot a lady. I'll give you all the money I've got!"

"Lady," The Misfit said, looking beyond her far into the woods, "there never was a body that give the undertaker a tip."

There were two more pistol reports and the grandmother raised her head like a parched old turkey hen crying for water and called, "Bailey Boy, Bailey Boy!" as if her heart would break.

"Jesus was the only One that ever raised the dead," The Misfit continued, "and He shouldn't have done it. He thown everything off balance. If He did what He said, then it's nothing for you to do but thow away everything and follow Him, and if He didn't, then it's nothing for you to do but enjoy the few minutes you got left the best way you can—by killing somebody or burning down his house or doing some other meanness to him. No pleasure but meanness," he said and his voice had become almost a snarl.

"Maybe He didn't raise the dead," the old lady mumbled, not knowing what she was saying and feeling so dizzy that she sank down in the ditch with her legs twisted under her.

"I wasn't there so I can't say He didn't," The Misfit said. "I wisht I had of been there," he said, hitting the ground with his fist. "It ain't right I wasn't there because if I had of been there I would of known. Listen lady," he said in a high voice, "if I had of been there I would of known and I wouldn't be like I am now." His voice seemed about to crack and the grandmother's head cleared for an instant. She saw the man's face twisted close to her own as if he were going to cry and she murmured, "Why you're one of my babies. You're one of my own children!" She reached out and touched him on the shoulder. The Misfit sprang back as if a snake had bitten him and shot her three times through the chest. Then he put his gun down on the ground and took off his glasses and began to clean them.

Hiram and Bobby Lee returned from the woods and stood over the ditch, looking down at the grandmother who half sat and half lay in a puddle of blood with her legs crossed under her like a child's and her face smiling up at the cloudless sky.

Without his glasses, The Misfit's eyes were red-rimmed and pale and defenseless-looking. "Take her off and thow her where you thown the others," he said, picking up the cat that was rubbing itself against his leg.

"She was a talker, wasn't she?" Bobby Lee said, sliding down the ditch with a yodel.

"She would of been a good woman," The Misfit said, "if it had been somebody there to shoot her every minute of her life."

"Some fun!" Bobby Lee said.

"Shut up, Bobby Lee," The Misfit said. "It's no real pleasure in life."

STUDY QUESTIONS

1. What is the theme of this story?
2. What American values are expressed in this story? Which of these values seem to be conducive to violence?
3. What do the names Red Sammy Butts, June Star, John Wesley, and Bobby Lee suggest about the characters and of the values they live by? Some of the characters are barely sketched in. What is the effect of this technique?
4. Is there evidence of sentimentality in the actions and attitudes of the family? Can sentimentality contribute to violence? How?
5. What function is served in terms of plot, theme, and character-ization by the stop at The Tower?
6. What is the changing significance of the title? Can you find evidence of foreshadowing and anticipation in this story?
7. What is the point of view? What purpose is served by this point of view? What limitations does it place upon the story?
8. Reconstruct The Misfit's family background. In what ways can a family condition its members to violent behavior?

9. Read carefully the paragraph that begins with "Jesus was the only One that ever raised the dead." How close is the attitude expressed in this paragraph to Kirillov's ideas about God in *The Possessed*? What view of religion is expressed in the O'Connor story?

10. The grandmother says to The Misfit, "Why you're one of my babies. You're one of my own children." What do you think it means?

11. What kind of violence is depicted here? Can it be explained? Can we attribute such violence only to psychological causes? Explain. Does passive resistance or non-violence work against men like The Misfit?

14

WHAT WE DON'T KNOW HURTS US*

Mark Schorer

Mark Schorer is a Professor of English and creative writing at the University of California at Berkeley. He is widely known for his William Blake: The Politics of Vision *and* Sinclair Lewis: An American Life, *and a collection of short stories,* The State of Mind. *In this story the lack of trust and the misconceptions between father and son lead to a conflict and estrangement that is perhaps beyond resolution.*

THE MIDAFTERNOON WINTER sun burned through the high California haze. Charles Dudley, working with a mattock in a thicket of overgrowth, felt as steamy and as moldy as the black adobe earth in which his feet kept slipping. Rain had fallen for five days with no glimmer of sunshine, and now it seemed as if the earth, with fetid animation, like heavy breath, were giving all that moisture back to the air. The soil, or the broom which he was struggling to uproot, had a disgusting, acrid odor, as if he were tussling with some obscene animal instead of with a lot of neglected vegetation and suddenly an overload of irritations—the smell, the stinging sweat in his eyes, his itching skin, his blistering palms—made him throw the mattock down and come diving out of the thicket into the clearing he had already achieved.

"Is it hard?"

He looked up and saw Josephine, his wife, sitting on the railing of the balcony onto which the french doors of their bedroom opened. She was holding a dust mop, and a tea towel was wrapped around her head, and her face seemed pallid and without character, as it always did to Charles when she neglected to wear lipstick.

He snorted instead of replying, and wiped his muddy hands on the seat of his stiff new levis. Then he walked over to the short flight of steps that led up to the balcony from the garden, and lit a cigarette.

"It looks as though the ground levels out up there where you're working," Josephine said.

"Yes, it does. Somebody once had a terrace up there. It's full of overgrown geraniums that are more like snakes, and a lot of damned rose vines."

"You've got the pepper tree almost free. It's going to be very nice, isn't it?"

He looked up at the pepper tree, with its delicate, drooping branches and the long gray tendrils that hung down from the branches to the ground. He had chopped out the broom as far up the incline as the tree, and now he could see that a big branch of the eucalyptus at the very edge of the property had forced the top of the pepper tree to grow out almost horizontally from the main portion of its trunk. "Look at the damned thing!" he said.

"It's charming, like a Japanese print."

"I'm going to hate this house long before it's livable," he said.

"Oh, Charles!"

"I didn't want to buy a house. I never wanted to own any house. I certainly never wanted to own a miserable, half-ruined imitation of a Swiss chalet built on an incline that was meant for goats." Vehemently he flipped his cigarette up into the pile of brush he had accumulated.

Josephine stood up and shook out the dust mop. "Let's not go into all that again. There was no choice. It's no pleasure for me, either, living the way we are, nor is it for the children." She paused, and then added a cold supplement. "I sometimes think that your disinclination to own anything is a form of irresponsibility." She turned swiftly and went into the house.

He stood staring after her, frowning a little, for it seemed momentarily that with studied intent she had cracked the bland habit of her amiability. But in a minute she reappeared in the doorway and said matter-of-factly, "I heard on the radio that Boston has had eighteen inches of snow." Then she went back inside.

"Are you trying to make me homesick?" he asked of no one as he started back up the incline, and he remembered the frozen river, snow blowing over the Esplanade, and city lights faint in a blizzard.

He began again to chop at the roots of the broom. All right, he told himself, so he was being unpleasant. He did not like the idea of being pinned down by a mortgage to a place his firm had picked for him. He did not even like the idea of being pinned down by a mortgage. To own something was, to that extent, to be owned, and he did not like the feeling. His idea of a good way to live was in a duplex apartment owned by someone else, in Charles River Square, or, better than that but always less likely, in a duplex apartment owned by someone else, on the East River. He connected happiness with a certain luxury, and, probably, sexuality with elegance and freedom. These were not noble associations, he was aware, and he knew that it was foolish to let impossibilities, as they faded, become forms of minor torture. This knowledge made him chop more angrily than ever at the broom.

It was vegetation with which Charles felt that he had a peculiar intimacy, perhaps the only thing in California which, in the several weeks they had lived there, he had really come to know. And he loathed it with a violence which he recognized as quite undue, and which, now, made him feel childish and curiously guilty. Yet he could not laugh away his loathing. The stuff was ubiquitous, and sprang up anywhere at all the minute the ground was neglected. If it grew up in a patch, it began a foolish competition with itself, and the thin, naked stalks shot ten and twelve and fourteen feet into the air, all stretching up to the sun for the sake of a plume of paltry foliage at the top. Then the foliage tangled together in a thatch, and when you had managed to chop out the shallow roots of the tree, you still had to extricate its trivial but tenacious branches from those of all its neighbors to get it out of the clump. Once it was out, the wood was good for nothing, but dried up into a kind of bamboo stalk so insubstantial that it did not make even decent kindling. As a tree it was a total fraud, and in spite of the nuisance of its numbers, and of its feminine air of lofty self-importance, it was, with its shallow roots in this loose soil, very vulnerable to attack. Charles beat away at it in an angry frenzy, as if he were overwhelming, after a long struggle, some bitter foe.

He did not hear his son come up the incline behind him, and the boy stood quietly watching until his father turned to toss a stalk up on the pile in the clearing. Then the boy said, "Hi." He said it tentatively, almost shyly, as though his father's responses were unpredictable.

"Hi, Gordon."

"What're you doing?"

"Can't you see? How was school?"

"It stinks," he answered doggedly, his dark eyes half-averted and sorrowful.

Charles felt a twinge of pain for him. "Cheer up. Give it time. You'll get to like it after a while."

"I'll never like it," Gordon said stubbornly.

Charles took up his mattock again. "Sure you will," he said as he began to swing it.

"Nobody likes me."

Charles let the mattock come to rest and, turning once more to the boy, he spoke with an impatient excess of patience. "You say that every day. I've told you it isn't true. You're a new boy in the school, and you came in the middle of the term, and there's never yet been a new boy who entered a school late and made friends right away. You're nearly nine, and you can understand that. Anyway, I'm tired of explaining it to you."

"When can I get a paper route?"

Charles laughed without humor. "My God, boy! Give us a chance to get settled."

"I need money."

"You get an allowance."

"I need more money," the boy insisted. "I want a paper route. How do kids get them?"

"You can work for me. You can get in there with a hedge shears and cut out all those vines."

The boy looked at his father despairingly and shook his head. "No, I need a lot of money."

"You can earn a lot of money working for me," Charles said, swinging his mattock.

"I need a dollar," Gordon said faintly.

His father did not hear him, and he did not turn from his work again until presently he heard his daughter calling him shrilly from the foot of the hill on which the house stood.

"What is it?" he called back. She was climbing the path, and he saw that she had a white envelope in her hand.

Then Gordon broke into rapid, desperate speech. "I need a dollar. I'll pay it back out of my allowance. Remember yesterday I told you about that dollar I found? I have to pay it back."

Charles stared at him. "What dollar?"

Gordon glanced wildly over his shoulder. His sister, holding the menacing white envelope in one hand and her workman's tin lunch box in the other, was halfway up the hill, coming along the side of the house. Pleadingly, Gordon looked back at his father. "The dollar; Remember? I told you I found it. You wanted to know what I did with it."

"What dollar?"

He sighed. "You didn't listen! You never listen!"

Charles patted his shoulder. "Now take it easy. Don't get excited. Tell me again. I don't think you told me anything about a dollar yesterday."

"The dollar I found. You asked me what I did with it, and I told you I gave it to Crow, and you said I should have brought it home to you."

"That Crow! I thought you were joking."

Penelope, the six-year-old, was behind him now, and Gordon's shoulders sagged in despair. "I wasn't joking," he said almost wearily as Penelope handed his father the letter. "You never really listen."

Charles read the precise handwriting on the envelope. "Mr. or Mrs. Dudley," it said, and in the lower left-hand corner, "Courtesy of Penelope." He opened the envelope and read the message:

DEAR MR. AND MRS. DUDLEY,

Gordon became involved in some difficulty about a dollar today, and I wish you would help me. The dollar was lunch money belonging to a girl who said she left it deep in her coat pocket, in the cloakroom, yesterday. When I brought it up with Gordon, he immediately said that he did not steal it. He says that he found it on the floor, and he also says that he told his father about it yesterday and that his father said he should have brought it home to him, and now he is fixed in his confusions. He gave it to an older boy named Will Crow, who spent it, and I have told Gordon that he will have to return a dollar to the girl tomorrow. Gordon is a very worthwhile little personality, but I do not think he has been entirely happy here at the Crestview School, and therefore, if you can help me straighten this out to his own best interest, I will be ever so grateful.

Sincerely yours,
GERTRUDE GRANDJENT,
Principal.

Charles groaned in exasperation. "My God, why did you have to drag me into it? What will that woman think?"

Gordon's lips were trembling. "You remember? I did tell you, didn't I?"

"Yes, I remember now. I remember very clearly that you told me you found it on the way to school, and when I asked you what you did with it, and you said you gave it to Crow, naturally I said you should have brought it home. *Listen*, Gordon—" The very simplicity of the boy's strategy infuriated Charles, and it was with an effort that he controlled his temper. He said, "Penny, you go in now and tell your mother you're home."

Penny was staring at her brother. "What did Gordon do?"

"Run along, Penny, as I told you."

She went down the incline reluctantly, staring back over her shoulder, and when she had gone into the house, Charles turned to Gordon again and said, "Sit down."

They sat down side by side on the damp slope. Gordon said, "Will you lend me a dollar and keep my allowance until it's made up? I have to take it back tomorrow."

"We'll talk about that later." Charles tapped the letter with his muddy hand. "Why did you tell me you found it in the street?"

Gordon looked away but answered promptly. "I knew if I told you I found it in school, you'd have said I should have taken it to the office."

"So you lied to me instead. That was better?"

Gordon did not answer.

"Answer me."

"Yes."

"Yes, what?"

"I lied."

That was that. Charles started over. "Why did you tell Miss Grandjent that you did not steal it when she hadn't even said that you had?"

"I knew that's what she thought."

"How did you know?"

"I just knew."

Charles hesitated. When he spoke again, his voice was warmer, friendly, almost confidential. "What's the little girl's name, Gordon?"

"She's not little. She's in high fourth."

"What's her name?"

"I don't know. Joan, I guess."

"What color is her coat?"

Gordon glanced at his father sharply. "I don't know. I never noticed it."

Charles bit his lip in exasperation and stood up. "Let's go inside." He led the way in.

Josephine was standing on a chair in the middle of the living room. She was dusting the hideous chandelier of dark metal and colored glass which hung from the center of the ceiling. It was only one of many distasteful features in the house which the Dudleys hoped to rid it of, but it was hard to find men to do all the necessary work, and none would promise to do it quickly. An electrician had torn away a good deal of plaster and lathing, and a carpenter had ripped out some bookshelves and ugly mantels and taken down most of a wall between the dining room and a useless hallway, but neither had returned, and painters, plasterers, paper hangers had not yet come at all. The Dudleys had decided to leave most of their belongings in storage until the work was done, and to bring nothing out of storage that they cared about. The result was that the house was almost fantastically disordered and bleak and squalid, and while Josephine managed to keep an even temper under these conditions, Charles, who found them very trying, did not.

He stood in the doorway of the living room now and said to her, "Why do you bother?"

"The light was so dim," she said, and then, seeing his expression, asked quickly, "What's wrong?"

"Another problem." He came heavily into the living room and gave her the letter. She read it standing on the chair, her face expressionless. Then she stepped down and went into the hall where Gordon was lurking and said, "Come in, dear."

There was one old sofa in the room, and Josephine sat down there with Gordon. Charles sat facing them on the single straight chair. Josephine took Gordon's hands and said, "Now tell me everything, Gordon, just the way it happened."

The boy's face was composed in a kind of stolid determination, but when he raised his moody eyes from the bare floor to his father, his chin began to tremble, his eyelids fluttered, and suddenly the dogged expression broke in despair, his body sagged, his head fell back against the sofa, and he burst into harsh sobs. Josephine put her arm around his shoulders and held him close while he cried, and she shook her head sharply at Charles as he jumped up impatiently. He sat down again. Finally Gordon stopped crying, almost as abruptly as he had begun.

"How did it happen, Gordon?" his mother asked.

He straightened up and stared at the floor again. "Nothing happened. I just came in the cloakroom and saw it on the floor. I took it and put it in my pocket, and at recess I gave it to Crow."

"Didn't anyone see you pick it up?"

"There wasn't anyone else there."

"In the cloakroom? Before school? Why not?"

"I was late."

"Late? But why? You left here in plenty of time."

"I stopped on the way and played with a cat."

Josephine frowned. "So there was no one else there at all to see you?" she asked meaningfully.

"No."

Josephine glanced at Charles. He drew his lips apart and, with a heavy satiric edge, said, "Well, Gordon, that's too bad! If there'd been someone else there, you could prove that you hadn't—"

Josephine broke in. "Tell me just where the dollar was, Gordon," she said softly, and her voice had no relation to the look in her eyes as she glanced at Charles.

"On the floor."

"But exactly where? Was it near the little girl's coat?"

"She isn't little."

"Was it near her coat?"

"I don't know which coat is hers."

"Was it near any coat?"

"It was on the floor, near all of them. They hang on a rack, and it was on the floor near them."

Josephine paused, and Gordon wriggled his shoulders out from under her arm and slumped in the corner of the sofa, away from her. "When can I get out of here?" he asked.

"When you start answering our questions," his father said sharply. "You insist that you didn't steal it?"

Gordon raised his lids slowly, as if they were very heavy, and stared out at his father from under his brows. "I found it on the floor."

Josephine spoke brightly. "Very well. We have settled that. But, Gordon, surely you don't think that because you found it on the floor, it belonged to you? Don't you see that it was just as much stealing it as if you had really taken it from the pocket of the person it belonged to?"

"Not as much," Gordon said.

"But it wasn't *yours!* You knew that."

The boy nodded.

"Well, then—"

"Someone else would have found it!"

"But would someone else have kept it?"

"I didn't keep it."

Charles leaped up from his chair. "That's the point! Why in God's name did you give it to that Crow rat?"

"He's my friend," Gordon said with simple defiance, and then he slid off the sofa and lay on the floor.

"Your friend! A fine friend!" Charles shouted in disgust, standing over him. "Get up!"

Gordon did not make any effort to move, and Josephine grasped Charles's arm. "Let me," she said quietly. "Sit down."

"Nonsense!" he cried angrily at her, and pulled his arm free of her touch. "I'll take over now." He seized the boy by the shoulders and pulled him up on the sofa. The jerk which he gave his body made the boy's head bob back and forward like a doll's, and he slumped against the sofa back almost as if he had been injured, dull eyes staring out of his pale face. "Now listen to me, Gordon. I don't know if you took that money out of someone's pocket or not, but it looks, from the way you're behaving, as if you did. Anyway, you took it. It didn't belong to you, you knew that, and yet you took it. Do you see that there is no difference between the floor and the pocket as long as you kept it?"

"I didn't keep it," Gordon repeated, but almost listlessly.

"Oh, my God!" Charles ran his hand through his hair, and the rumpled hair gave him a sudden wild look. "Listen," he said as quietly as he could, "we are all having a very hard time here. We are trying to live in a house that isn't fit to live in. I am trying to get used to a new office. Your mother—"

Josephine said, "Don't bother about me."

"I will bother! We're all having a tough time, and Gordon can't think of anything better to do than to get into this mess at school. Of all the friends you could pick, you pick that nasty Crow brat, who is too old for you by three years and is a snide little—"

"Charles!"

Gordon lay back on the sofa. He looked ill and defeated.

"Will you admit that you stole that dollar? That taking it from the floor was just as much stealing it as if you had taken it from the pocket?"

"Yes," he answered faintly.

"Speak up!"

"Yes, I *do!*" Gordon cried, and turned his face away.

Then the room was very still. Josephine stood stiffly beside the couch, her eyes fixed on Charles with dismay. Charles sagged a little, as if he, too were defeated. And Gordon might have been asleep or dreaming, so remote had he suddenly become. Then they all heard a sly noise at the door, and Charles and Josephine swung toward it. Penelope stood there, embarrassed to have been caught. She giggled and said, "Why did Gordon steal money?"

"Go away," Charles said.

"Go to your room, dear," Josephine said, "or go outside."

"But why did Gordon steal money?"

Charles walked to the girl, gave her a little push, and closed the door on her face. Then he came back to the sofa. He sat down next to Gordon, and when he spoke, his voice was nearly lifeless. "You want to earn that dollar. All right, you can, Gordon. First go to your room and write your five sentences. Do them quickly for a change, and then go out into that patch of broom with the hedge shears and cut down all the vines you can find in it. You have an hour left before it gets dark."

Gordon's eyes dreamed over his father's face, and then he slowly got up and left the room. His parents watched him go, and when he had closed the door softly behind him, Charles broke out. "What is it, what stubbornness, that makes that boy so impenetrable. Did he steal that money or not? I haven't the slightest idea. All I could do was force him to admit that there was no difference between the two things."

Josephine was looking at him with studied appraisal.

"Well?" he challenged her.

"You forced his admission. Did that gain anything? And what did it lose? How much did it hurt him? Is it of very great importance whether he stole it or not?"

"I don't know what's more important."

"No, I really think you don't."

"Well?"

"What's more important is why he took it, and what he did with it, and why he did that. What's more important is that he's a miserable little boy, and that you haven't made the slightest effort to understand *that*. All you've done is played the heavy parent, shown him that you don't trust him or believe him, and left him with a nice new layer of solidified guilt, and what is he supposed to do with *that?*"

"Let's skip the psychology for a change," Charles said. "There is an old-fashioned principle of honesty and dishonesty."

"There's a more old-fashioned one of simple perception." Josephine's face was red with anger. She stood in the middle of the bare room and looked rapidly around her, as if she felt a sudden desperate need, a hunger, for objects. But there was only the sofa, the chair, and Charles. Her eyes came back to him.

"Have you thought of his difficulties at all? Just the simple matter of his writing, for example? He came from a school where the children printed, and he printed as well as anyone. He comes here where the children do cursive writing, and of course he's made to feel like a fool, and he has to practice at home to learn it when other boys are playing. Or have you once helped him with that? Have you even suggested a sentence he might write? No. All you've done is to give him the extremely comforting bit of information that new boys, especially if they enter school late, have a hard time making friends! The one friend he has made you deride. No, don't interrupt. I know he's a horrid boy. I don't want Gordon playing with him either. But you haven't the sense to see that what has brought them together is that they are both pariahs. I think Gordon's giving that dollar to that dreadful boy is one of the most touching things I've ever heard of!"

"If what you've told me about Crow is true," Charles said quietly, "I won't have Gordon playing with him, and that's that."

"Because Crow taught him some nasty words and told him some nasty, mistaken things about sex! You're perfectly right. But you can't just stand there and say no to him! If you were half a father, you would have told him yourself. You should be his friend! You're the one who should be giving him a decent attitude toward those things. You *are* his father, after all."

"Oh, listen—He's not even nine!"

"All right. But he's getting it, isn't he? And all wrong?" And then without warning, she sat down heavily on the single chair and began to sob, her reddened face lifted, her mouth twisted in sorrow, tears streaming down over her cheeks. "All *wrong!*" she wailed.

Charles went to her quickly and, half standing, half kneeling beside the chair, awkwardly put his arms around her. "Josephine, listen?"

"Oh, I know!" she sobbed. "We all get in your way. We're all a nuisance that you're saddled with! We all just *bother* you! I know! It just isn't your idea of the way to live. You really hate it, don't you?"

His arms tightened. "Darling," he said, "don't be a damned fool. Listen, I love you, I love the kids. Why, little Penny, I—"

"Oh, yes, Penny, sure! She's tractable! She doesn't raise any problems. That's different!"

"You're crazy. Gordon, too. You. Maybe I'm not much good with him, but that doesn't mean . . . And listen . . . I'll try. I'll go out there now."

She dug in her pocket for a piece of Kleenex. She blew her nose and wiped her eyes. She pulled the tea towel off her head and shook out her hair. Then she blew her nose again. "I'm all right now," she said, getting up. She picked up the dustcloth which she had flung over the back of the chair, and she said, "It's probably just this awful house, the way we have to camp. I'm going to get cleaned up and dress, and I'm going to find a table cloth, and we'll have dinner at a table tonight, instead of sitting on the floor with plates in our laps."

He said, "Good girl! I'll go and fix it up with Gordon."

Charles went into Gordon's room. It was empty. He glanced at the table where Gordon worked and saw that there was a sheet of writing there. Then he looked out the window and saw the boy on his hands and knees in among the remaining broom. He crossed the hall to the bedroom where Josephine was dressing. "I may not be very subtle with him, but I seem to get results," he said. She merely glanced up at him, and as he went out on the balcony, down the steps, and up the slippery incline, he felt no satisfaction whatever in his remark.

"How's it going?" he asked the boy.

Gordon glanced over his shoulder. "All right," he said, and turned at once to his job. The hedge shears made a busy, innocent sound.

Charles found his mattock where he had dropped it, and began to chop at the edge of the overgrowth again. Immediately his nostrils filled with the poisonous smell he had noticed before, his hands began to chafe, and even though the heat of the sun had gone in the late afternoon, sweat broke out with a prickling sensation all over his face and body. Once more he was tense with irritation, and he said, "That awful smell! What is it?"

"I don't know," Gordon replied without looking up.

"Like something decaying."

The boy did not answer, and Charles chopped angrily away at a root. When it came free, he shook the earth off and tossed the slim tree down the slope. "This crazy, piddling stuff!" he shouted, and then reminded himself that it was only a kind of exaggerated weed, a thing that grew everywhere, so futile that it could not even send him down a decent root and was hardly designed as a personal affront to him. Or was it? He laughed and started to chop at the next root, but stopped at once. "I'm quitting for today," he said. "Come on, let's go in."

Gordon said, "No, I'll work a while. I want to earn the money."

"Oh, let it go. We'll fix that up."

Gordon stared at him. "I want to earn it," he said, and went on clipping at the rose vines.

"All right," Charles said, "but come in soon. You'll have to wash up thoroughly to get that muck off."

He went back into the house by way of the bedroom, but Josephine was no longer there. He went into Gordon's room, but she was not there, either. On the table lay the white sheet of ruled paper covered with the boy's writing, his five sentences in their hasty, uncertain, and very large cursive characters. Charles picked it up. The first sentence was, "I am going to cut vins." The second was, "I am going to ern mony." The third was, "The sun is shining." The fourth was, "When it rains here it rains hard." The last, which seemed to have been written with great care, with a kind of precision and flourish which his writing had never shown before, was, "You hate me and I hate you."

Charles took a sharp breath and held it, then sagged. After a moment he walked to the window and put his forehead against the cool glass. He stared out into the desolate garden, at the bare earth and the darkening tangle, and tried to think. When he heard Josephine moving on high heels somewhere in the rugless house, he began to fold the sheet of paper, and he folded it again and again, until it was a small hard square. This he stuffed deep into his pocket.

He came into the hall and saw Josephine standing in the center of the barren living room. She looked tall in an old but still handsome black housecoat, a straight, severe garment which hung from the tightly belted waist in heavy folds, and was without ornament or color anywhere. Her hair was pulled tautly away from her face, and her face was smooth and white, and her mouth was painted dark red.

She was detached from the room, from the house, and utterly from him—remote and beautiful, cold in resolution. Never in the ten years he had known her had she appeared so wonderfully in possession of herself. And, helplessly, Charles turned away.

He went into the boy's room again, and looked out to see the boy. But twilight had obscured the garden now, shadows hung about it like veils, and Charles could hardly see into the trees. Then he thought that he saw Gordon's shape, hunched on the ground among the slim trunks, and he went out quickly to find him. Perhaps, even now, after everything, it was the boy who, somehow, could help.

STUDY QUESTIONS

1. Define *psychological violence*. Give as many illustrations as you can of psychological violence. To what extent can we say that there is psychological violence in this story?

2. Before Gordon appears in the story, there is a long introduction which focuses on the father. What purposes does this introduction serve? What does it reveal about Charles Dudley? What relationships do you see between frustrations and violence?

3. What do you see as the relationship between Charles Dudley's attitude toward the vegetation and toward his son?

4. Trace the series of frustrations and conflicts in Charles Dudley's life.

5. Which character in the story seems to suffer the most from psychological violence?

6. Where in society and in your own experience have you seen evidence of psychological violence? Can psychological violence strike deeper and be more damaging to the human personality than physical violence?

7. The last sentence of this story poses a paradox. Explain.

ESSAY QUESTIONS

1. Write an essay describing some act of violence out of your own experience, and analyze its causes, or write an essay in which a certain set of circumstances in your personal life or in your community could lead to violence.

2. Write an essay justifying the use of violence or non-violence.

3. Write an essay defending the thesis that man is naturally violent.

4. Write a paper giving your explanation of the violent killings of President Kennedy, Senator Kennedy, and Martin Luther King.

5. Write a paper giving your own definitions of violence? Does it disagree with that of Garver or Audi?

6. Write a paper defending the thesis that violence will increase or decrease in the foreseeable future in America.

7. Write an essay on the relationship of the Viet Nam war to violence in the American society.

8. Select an ancient myth in which violence occurs and show why the myth is meaningful in today's world.

9. Compare and contrast the violence of Sgt. Croft in "I Hate Everything Which is Not in Myself" with the violence of the intruders in "A Good Man is Hard to Find."

10. Compare and contrast the causes of violence in "Prishchepa" and "The Prussian Officer."

11. Describe and explain a non-physical act of violence from your own experience.

12. Discuss the artistic appropriateness of violence on television programs.

13. Using the essays of this book as your source, explain the nature and causes of the violence in one of the short stories.

14. Write an essay in which you delineate the possible causes of individual, social, and national violence.

15. Write a paper in which you argue for or against the mass media and sports as contributors to the climate of violence in our society.

16. Write an essay outlining your proposals for the elimination of some aspect of violence in yourself, your community, or the nation.

17. Write an essay, based on the fiction selections in this book, in which you argue that violence is either natural or conditioned in man.

18. Write a narrative in which you depict an act of violence. Then write a paper explaining the appropriateness of your use of violence.

19. We know that violence is world wide. Write a paper in which you attempt to show through the short stories what seems to you to be peculiarly American about violence.

20. "Violence results from personal failure."
    "Violence is an attempt to right some wrong."
    Justify one of the statements above using fiction as your sources.

FURTHER READINGS

Ardrey, Robert. *African Genesis; The Territorial Imperative.*

Arendt, Hannah. *On Violence.*

Bienan, Henry. *Violence and Social Change.*

Brown, Richard Maxwell, ed. *American Violence.*

Erikson, Erik H. *Gandhi's Truth: On the Origins of Militant Nonviolence.*

Fanon, Frantz. *The Wretched of the Earth.*

Frohock, W. M.*The Novel of Violence in America, 1920-1950.*

Gray, Glenn J. *The Warriors: Reflections on Men in Battle.*

Graham, Hugh Davis and Ted Robert Gurr, eds. *The History of Violence in America.*

Gurr, Ted Robert. *Why Men Rebel.*

Lorenz, Konrad. *On Aggression.*

Mayer, Peter, ed. *The Pacifist Conscience.*

Miller, William Robert. *Nonviolence: A Christian Interpretation.*

Montagu, Ashley M. F., ed. *Man and Aggression.*

Rose, Thomas, ed. *Violence in America.*

Shaffer, Jerome, ed. *Violence.*

Wolff, Robert Paul. "On Violence." (*Journal of Philosophy,* Vol. LXVI, (1969), pp. 601-616.)

Wolff, B. Moore, Jr., and H. Marcuse, eds. *A Critique of Pure Tolerance.*

W